Pelé
Can Wait

P.S. HONEY

Pelé Can Wait, Copyright © P.S. Honey 2024
ISBN 978-1-915962-44-7

First published 2024 by Compass-Publishing UK

Edited by AJ Humpage
Typeset by The Book Refinery Ltd

This book is not a work of fiction. There are deep scars to prove it.

Names, characters, places and incidents are either a product of the author's
experience or have been artistically modified so that the chances of being
sued for defamation of character have been significantly reduced. Any resem-
blance to actual people living or dead, events or locales is entirely possible.

A CIP catalogue record for this book is available from the
British Library.

For Ali.

I'm sorry for putting you through the scariest time of our lives.
And, for reliving it for a second time within the pages of this book.

Contents

1

'Ding, Ding' Round One

Friday, June 25th, 2021, was the day Pelé was put on hold. Well, not the great man himself, but the acrylic-based portrait I had been lovingly painting for my own benefit. I had discovered a love of painting a couple of years before that date, and no, it wasn't brought on during the great lockdown of 2020. Although, it would have been fair to say that during that time I did churn out a load of awful artwork and came out the other side. You learn by your mistakes. I'd always been my harshest critic, and devilishly modest too, so I couldn't say I was fantastic, but on the other hand, I had sold some portraits, so I wasn't completely useless. I loved the escapism and tranquillity it brought me during the creation stage. Good job I wasn't baking banana bread at the time everything happened because 'The Banana Bread Can Wait' sounded like a terrible book.

My personal tribute to Pelé certainly could wait. It had to; it had no choice.

I'd suffered a terrible night's sleep. I had always been a good sleeper, yet I must have been up at least a dozen times throughout the night to go for a wee. It wasn't like me at all. As someone that had recently hit 50 years old just eight weeks prior (congratulations to me, thank you), I had been used to getting up during the night once and sometimes twice, but I could equally sleep right through without a pit stop as well. I knew something was up. I'd eaten a kebab the night before and that hadn't sat right with me. I felt a bit constipated, but more than that, I knew that I had some sort of infection that had made me feverish.

After speaking to Ali, my beautiful and long-suffering wife of twenty-two years, I took her advice and got on the phone to the Doctor. It seemed like a course of antibiotics were very much required ASAP. The truth was, any A&E department over a weekend was no party, so I needed to get to the GP before that became necessary.

I didn't blame that innocent chicken shish wrap or the friendly Turkish guys in the local shop that made it. I'd better clarify that it was just a little treat for the family and there's no outrageous wild story about me going out with GaryMan (my best mate since we were twelve) and the rest of the guys, on the razzle, getting hammered and ending up staggering around a dirty kebab van – all on a school night. Not much point in me fabricating the truth to sound cool, like I was thirty years ago.

The truth was – it was an innocent family takeaway.

The last meal before time stood still.

And yes, I was cool thirty years ago.

Obviously, I conquered the automated telephone system, and I finally got an appointment arranged with Dr Shabani (they always give me the new Doctors) for 1pm at the local GP surgery. They were only a short drive away so it was all wonderfully convenient.

After I said goodbye to Ali and our three children, as they ventured out into the scary zombie apocalyptic (AKA pandemic) world to work and school, I barely creaked along that morning. I had done my lateral flow test to check for Covid, along with government guidelines, and found I was clean. For the time being.

Ali became the family's designated Covid Queen. She knew the rules and, like a lioness, had done everything she could to protect the pride. She may have been the shortest in the house, all five feet nothing of her, but she had always been a passionate and caring woman and with her kind blue eyes and pretty smile, I (and the rest of the family) always did as we were told. Mission Impossible would be to say no to Ali.

Our offspring were an even and healthy mixture of our genes. All three children had dark features (Ali and I were both brunettes and could pass for Europeans from the Mediterranean when we sported summer tans) but Ali was the odd-one out with her eye colour, since the rest of us had a different shade of brown, because my genes kept winning the conception battle. Harrison (Harri) was our eldest at twenty-two (so not exactly a child), with average height, a slim build, and a classically handsome face, which I would say, because he looked the most like me. Without any doubt, he was the brains of the family. As I told whoever wanted to know, Harri was a class act. He was just like me, only a hundred times better.

Our middle child was Jayden (Jay). He had done his best to grow taller than his dad but seemed to have settled at an impressive six foot, an inch short of the target. He was nineteen and he had always been the sporty one (football mad) and so he had a far more muscular build than his elder brother. Jay had a lovely face and a round nose that he inherited from his mother's side of the family. It's the noses that define which parental side those kids came from. Harri definitely had a slightly longer, sharper Honey nose, whilst Jay was blessed with a Duncan nose which was more like a teddy bear's. Jay was a lot more like Ali, which might be why I got on with him so well. Opposites attract they say. He was so easy-going (horizontal), affectionate and hilarious whenever he chose to be.

Finally, our little surprise made from love, was Lydia (Lyds). Our youngest and only daughter was a great mix of her parents' traits and a perfect combination of feisty and fun. Still at school at the difficult age of thirteen, she seemed to be a typical girl with her head locked into her iPhone for 95% of her waking hours. She was already a couple of inches taller than Ali, with a graceful and slim build, and fortunate enough to be blessed with her mother's pretty face and smile, rather than my ugly mug. Beautiful and great fun to be around, she was destined to become a total heartbreaker when she got older, of that, I was sure.

With the family busy, I was alone. I felt hot, constipated, sluggish, and thought I was generally running at about 20% at best. The sensation in my lower abdomen wasn't pain exactly, but I was uncomfortable, and it was an unfamiliar feeling. I was concerned that I had some infection that needed treatment and wondered if it was the start of a full-blown sickness and fever. Going to the toilet throughout the night had not been normal. I did my best to dismiss any worries and tried the art of distraction as I responded to a couple of emails and made a few calls. I cancelled an important meeting that clashed with the 1pm appointment at the surgery. My bowels continued to groan and grumble and drag my mood down. I knew it wasn't the familiar preambles associated with a bout of diarrhoea, which had to be a good thing at least.

At that point, I still had about 26 hours to go until I reached THAT time.

The GP

When it hit 12:45pm, I put on a zip-up top over my T-shirt and rammed a cap on my head. I felt in a grumpy mood as I knew that the weekend plans had flown completely out of the window. I just knew my body was failing somewhere and I knew a bout of illness headed my way. When I arrived at the GP's surgery everything seemed good. I parked up, put my mask on, pushed the intercom and I think it was friend-of-the-family Angela on the desk that let me in, but I could be wrong there as I've tried not to get too over-friendly because I don't want them knowing everything about me. But they love it, the power, on that desk, don't they? When we call, we just want to see a doctor but in order to do that we have to go through the newly accepted protocol of being waterboarded via the phone.

'What exactly is the problem with your erectile dis-function, Mr Pelé?'

'Really? Can I just discuss this with the Doctor please?'

'No Mr Pelé, I have to put every intimate detail on the system so please just answer the question.'

Like a good boy, I checked in using the wall-fixed tablet, sanitised my hands, sat on the almost comfortable plastic chair in the socially distanced waiting room and realised I felt worse than I did before. Unusual for me – every other time I made it to the doctor, I ended up feeling a bit better and then I'd feel like a fraud in front of the Doctor and I would say, 'Well it was bad yesterday.' I was one of those people that didn't stay ill in front of the GP.

The wait was neither long nor short. My name flashed up on the screen and I made my way down to Room 7 – Dr Shabani. With everyone masked up, it was tricky to make a proper connection, but she truly was as kind as her eyes appeared and asked all the right questions. I felt that all was going to plan and I'd soon be off to the pharmacy, prescription in hand. But she was being too kind. And she was being too concerned and she wanted to know more about my diabetes. I'd been diagnosed as Type 2 diabetic for about a year, which was the best variety – just one tablet every day, so I didn't have to inject insulin all the time like those Type 1 people (the real diabetics). She told me my temperature was high – 38.9 degrees. Strange, I'd done all that temperature and LFT business a couple of hours ago.

Don't let it be flipping Covid.

I'd had my first jab, so I felt optimistic that I had dodged that bullet. Dr Shabani took her time, but she didn't have the equipment around to check out my blood sugar levels, and she left me there to ask her colleagues in the surgery to help hunt down the testing equipment. Or so she said. Two minutes later she came back into the room and told me that she hadn't been able to track down the little hand-held machine she wanted.

'Mmm. OK,' she remarked as she tapped away on her keyboard. 'I really need to send you over to A&E. Just to check you over properly and make sure we aren't missing anything.'

A&E? Seriously? The whole point of me going to see the GP was to avoid the inevitable 8 hour wait in A&E over the weekend just to get some antibiotics. Wexham Park Hospital was really not that far, but that's not the point. Every time I've ever had the joy of entering that most depressing of establishments it has meant a loss of several hours – and there were a million better ways of spending a Friday afternoon-evening-night.

'Really?' I asked. 'Can't you just get me some antibiotics? I don't think it's quite so serious.'

'How did you get here? Did you drive?' she asked me.

I told her that I had indeed driven and in response she offered that she could arrange for an ambulance to take me to hospital. She was calm and determined.

Ambulance? Hang on. I really wasn't that ill. I was like most people - I hated the idea of using an ambulance just to cart me off to a place that was less than a five-minute drive away - they were for emergencies, not for people who felt a bit feverish. Picture the flashing blue lights, sirens blaring and paramedics rushing around screaming, 'He's tachycardic!'

'It's OK – they are expecting you. You can go straight through without the wait.'

I've been to Wexham Park's A&E twice for myself. Both related to injuries from my days of playing American Football. The first time, back in '91, had been a delayed reaction to a big hit in the ribs (yes, those helmets acted as protection *and* as weapons) when my breathing had turned so shallow and painful, I thought I'd broken a rib. Ali remembered the event as I sat on her bed at her mum and dad's house a couple of years before we moved in together and I calmly got up and announced that I was going to hospital.

'What?' she said with great surprise.

'Yep,' I whispered. 'I can't really breathe.'

Anyway, Ali drove me there and although it was around 10pm on a Monday, it was fairly busy, and I had to wait until gone midnight before I was seen by a doctor. Before being told that my ribs were well and truly bruised and there was bugger all I could do except take some anti-inflammatories and rest, I was shocked that some geezer with a cut knee had been rushed through in a wheelchair even though he came in after me. I shuffled up to the desk and in a tiny voice, I reminded the lady on reception that I couldn't breathe. Apparently, the ambulance cases took priority. Well, they did back then. I just had to sit there, barely able to breathe as I tried not to puke, which would have been unbearable.

Soon after came my second visit. There are many occasions where I learned a lot from those experiences. A year or two after the damaged ribs incident I had been playing again and towards the end of a particularly brutal game, the ambulance crew had wanted to take me to hospital for an X-ray on my lower leg. I knew it wasn't broken, but because my adrenaline was still racing around my body and because I'd learnt that I'd get priority treatment, I relented and let them take me to Wexham Park's A&E. That time the trip was a success all round. In and out within an hour (including the X-ray) and, as I'd hoped, no fracture. Most of the time we know our bodies, right? For the record, after several seasons with many more touchdowns than hospital visits, I hung up my shoulder pads and became a responsible parent.

So, it was now my third time. It's true that my concerns had changed. I really hadn't believed I was ill enough to warrant a trip to hospital, but the Doctor seemed quite determined that's what I needed.

'No. It's really OK. I can drive there,' I said. I wasn't feeling great but felt well enough to drive.

'I really don't think you should drive.' More concern from her.

I'd accepted that I probably should do as I was told. Now, I don't want to sound tight-fisted, but I didn't want to have to apply for a second mortgage to cover the inevitable car park charges so, at that point, I weighed up my logistical options.

Option 1. Leave my car at the GP Surgery and let their ambulance come and get me.

Option 2. Drive to the hospital myself – which left my car to the mercy of the extortionist car park machine.

Option 3. Drive home (five minutes) and get my middle one, Jayden, to drive me back and drop me off at the hospital and Ali would pick me up later once the quacks had seen me and sorted out my much-needed prescription.

The third option looked good to me. Let the ambulance be available for others and save it for a real emergency. I remembered the last time I called for an ambulance it had been a busy time - 10am on a Saturday morning, but it never turned up, and other parents and teammates helped me scrape Jayden off the football pitch and take him, and his dislocated kneecap, to Wexham Park. I sat there in the summer of 2021 and although not at the peak height of the panic of the Covid-19 pandemic, it was still a period of facemasks, sanitising everything, social distancing and people not going to hospitals if they could avoid it. Hospital beds were still in high demand from people that had suffered the dangerous symptoms associated with breathing difficulties.

I made three phone calls. First one was a fairly brief one to let Ali know that, after all, I had to go to hospital to get some medication.

'How are you though?'

'I'm OK, really,' was my reassuring reply. I did say it was a brief call.

Then I called Jay, who was at home. He was two months away from starting his apprenticeship, but as a relatively new driver, he didn't sound convinced that he wanted to be my taxi driver…but, alright, he would do it. Then I made a work call and spoke to one of my surveyors, Aleks, and asked her to cancel my 2pm meeting. I briefly explained why and said that my Friday afternoon looked like a complete write-off, but we'd catch up early next week and rearrange our diaries when I would be back.

Dr Shabani handed me a couple of sheets of paper for me to pass to whoever would be checking me in at the hospital and she wished me luck. I made my way out and as I went outside and into the sunshine, I walked towards my car and remembered how frustrated I felt about how the day had taken a turn I didn't want. I hoped that I was going to be at home, new pills in hand, to watch whatever match was on for the (delayed) Euro 2020 Round of 16. *Hang on*, I thought…no game tonight as it was a gap between the group stages and the knockouts. OK – so just a normal pandemic-esque Friday night then.

I modified Option 3. From the inexperienced teenager, I switched tactics to the over-qualified pensioner. My father-in-law (the legend) lived very near to the doctor's surgery. I drove there, parked along the road, as it was likely to stay there for several hours, and I made my way down the in-law's drive. Uncle Rob was there to help move some old furniture into or out of the garage. I say uncle, but Rob was technically my Common-Law Step-Uncle In-Law (not that there is such a thing) or Ali's aunt's partner of thirty-plus years to be just as confusing. He was a decent guy, always helping people, especially family, and he could probably tell, at that moment when I moped down the drive, that I was another person in need. I said hello and asked Rob if Bob was about (apologies for all the Roberts). Bob *was* about, and when he came outside to see what was going on, I asked him if he would take me hospital.

The most unselfish man in history said, 'Of course. Let's go!'

Before I knew it, we were on our way. We took a slight detour, mainly because the poor chap had been living with Alzheimer's for a while and his driving had been remarkably different compared to the last time he had driven me, but he got me there in one piece, bless him. He also wished me well and said he was there for me to get me home when I had finished at the hospital.

A&E

Facemask on, I entered the A&E building.

A couple of people were in front of me, so I awaited my turn. There were stickers on the floor meant to encourage social distancing, and everyone complied. After a couple of minutes, a member of staff beckoned me forward on to a plastic chair opposite the reception desk as I was next after the elderly woman in front. I glanced to the left and saw the dreaded waiting room. It didn't look too bad. When I had accompanied Ali there, several months before the Covid zombie apocalypse, we had sat there for more than eight hours – not a great prospect ahead of me. The elderly lady shuffled away to the waiting area and I approached the welcoming receptionist. I didn't particularly want to stand up and answer the standard questions, but I had to.

Name?

Philip Honey.

Date of Birth?

12th of the 3rd 1971.

Postcode? Shoe Size? Pin Number?

Blah. Blah. Blah.

She tapped away on her keyboard and talked to her colleagues behind the newly installed Perspex screens. She told me I wouldn't have to wait too long.

She wasn't kidding. My treatment was remarkably different. One of the porters guided me straight past the hundred seats in the waiting area, through some double doors and a short walk up to the triage desk. The desk addressed the porter with some small talk, and then they shared a nod and after I'd confirmed to them who I was, when I was born and where I lived, he showed me to a nice little bed in the corner.

I climbed on to the bed. That makes it sounds like it was much higher up than the average bed when it wasn't. I don't know how else to describe how I got onto the bed and I've made it seem like a proper ordeal, but in reality, I simply got onto the bed. I can report that once I lay on my back, I surveyed my new home and, compared to other examination rooms and areas, it looked an incredibly spacious Master Bedroom with seemingly modern equipment and I saw the open-plan layout to the two people on the front desk and a clear run to the toilet (not technically a plush and private ensuite), should I have needed it.

As grateful as I was that I had just queue-jumped several hours of waiting, I felt equally concerned about how much a priority I seemed to be for everyone there.

Within 5 minutes a nurse arrived and asked me to confirm my name, date of birth and post code. Flippin' 'eck, that was at least the third time since I had arrived. She busied around me and took some observations. She shoved an electronic thermometer into my right ear to take my temperature (I can't remember exactly how high it was as the procedure happened frequently throughout my stay). Next, I felt the dreaded Velcro cuff of the blood pressure monitor around my arm. Many of us have had blood pressure taken, but the hospital version was a mobile vertical chrome pole with a neat electrical box at waist height with tubes and cables that dangled from it. Once it was ready, it beeped as the box forced air into the cuff and squeezed my upper arm. But the squeeze kept going. The machine beeped constantly. And then it squeezed some more. I felt the deep pulse in my arm, and for a second, I thought, '*Oh shit, the machine is broken and it's going to keep squeezing and pushing until the blood vessels in my arm go pop!*'

I've thought these crazy thoughts every time. Then the machine made its final double-beep and I heard and felt the air release from the cuff, and I finally stopped thinking my arm would explode and returned to normal rational thinking. Seriously, if I didn't have high blood pressure before, the whole performance of having blood pressure taken conjured up enough stress to give me high blood pressure.

My readings were normal – nothing to worry about.

I say nothing to worry about, but the nurse immediately handed me a hospital gown to wear.

Crikey.

They said it was so that my top wouldn't get dirty and would be better for everyone when it came to doing tests and all of that.

Yeah, like when you rush me through for open-heart surgery, I thought. Just how bad was my blood pressure? I didn't fight it. I took off my top and put my arms into the gown.

Note to nursing staff – unless they suspect their patient is a professional, then they should give them a hand because trying to tie up a gown with a big split up the back was not easy for a gown-virgin like me.

I managed to get the thing tied up at the back of my neck, but the ties behind my lower back were not having it, so they just hung there. At least it was on as I got back onto the bed.

Whilst I struggled with my gown, another nurse stood beside me and set up various bits of kit I knew nothing about. He was a noticeably camp male nurse. He looked like a young student nurse, somewhere between 20 and 22, with Chinese heritage, and I guessed him to be around 5′ 4″. He also wanted to know all my details and declared that he loved my name. Normally, only the ladies loved Honey as a surname, but he proved to be the exception. I accepted his offer of a cup of water, thank you very much. His naturally black hair sported a fringe with bright blue highlights, which seemed to get in his eyes as he struggled to get a cannula into my left forearm.

Cannula?

That was a whole new experience for me. I reckon I was thinking about a catheter when the word first popped up. I soon understood that the cannula was a flexible needle-cum-tube designed to ensure liquids, such as saline or medication, could be administered directly into my vein via my arm, without nurses having to inject me every five minutes. It was a semi-permanent route into my bloodstream. Or was that semi-temporary?

So, the short, stocky, student male nurse (with the blue highlights) needed three goes to force the fucking needle-thing into my arm. He was desperately apologetic for the failed attempts. He also complimented me for my great veins and although there was an inuendo that lurked in there, it didn't excuse him sticking more pricks into me. I did not look at my arm where all the action took place, but I felt the scratch of the needle several times and I thought, '*Oh, for fuck sake.*'

For the record, I wasn't a squeamish person and where needles were concerned; I was pretty good. I'd donated blood many times and although the idea of what physically happened didn't feel nice, I'd say it wasn't painful, but rather more uncomfortable and once in place it was usually all OK after two seconds.

In the end we got there and eventually he taped it in place with proper hospital tape and I sat back with a nice pink cannula in place. I took a picture of it with my iPhone and sent it to Ali. Poor me, with a teary-eye emoji.

I hadn't brought many belongings with me. I'd put my phone and wallet on one of the adjustable tables that patients got as extra bit of furniture with their hospital bed. They were great for wheeling about and extending up and down. I placed the A4 sheet of paper from the GP on it, as well as the cup of water. I don't know how, but I had a bit of moment and managed to spill 98% of the water all over that report. Great. I did my best to salvage it. I tried to dry it on a combination of the bedsheets and my trouser leg. My new friend breezed by and I flagged him down to explain what had happened.

'Don't worry,' he said, and he helped mop up the water from the table. He replaced it with a new cup.

Let's try and keep the replacement in the upright position.

A new face entered my bedroom, a face that could have passed as N'Golo Kanté's dad. I had an annoying habit where I will pick out a celebrity look-a-like for pretty much everyone. Kanté was a French footballer, with West African heritage, blessed with a small, yet wiry physique. The man was dressed in hospital overalls and because he looked a generation older, the new arrival could easily have convinced me that N'Golo was his equally bald son. N'Golo senior had an efficient, intense demeanour that had been softened with a kind face, and he got straight to work.

Without any fuss he tied up my bicep, plumped up a vein and took some blood samples. That was more like it. He also told me in his gentle African voice that the hospital needed me to take a Covid test. Mouth open wide (me, not him), he probed the swab straight to the back of my mouth and expertly scraped away the necessary cells he needed. It was swiftly followed by that horrible up-the-nose second phase and then before I knew it, the stick was in the vial and it was all labelled up and off he went. I must have been negative as there was no come back from this. At that point I, and the rest of the family, had dodged Covid-19. We'd been good little boys and girls and followed the guidelines as well as anyone had done.

Before long, Kanté's dad returned with a bag of saline and a load of tubing. He hoisted it up high on another wheeled pole, but before I got plugged into the cannula, he brought out a syringe that contained a special clear saline solution. The truth is, I don't know if there was anything different or special about the contents of the syringe other than it was used first. The cannula had two entry points (I don't know if they ever have more) and Mr Kanté carefully attached the syringe to one of the entry points – for an idea of how big they were, picture the size of a packet of Extra Strong mints - and he flushed the contents through the cannula. He did it at a nice and steady pace. It was cool. Not in a funky way, but as in the temperature was chilly – I felt the coolness within a few inches of where the liquid entered my arm and then, I guess, the sensation only stayed localised as my body temperature engulfed the cooler solution.

Another new experience for me. Presumably it was to clear the way and sort out air bubbles and maybe correct kinks in the tube, I didn't know exactly why, I just know that it happened every time it was time to start up a new bag of liquid. Don't panic – I do not intend to write about every single flush or bag change – just the first one as it was all new to me. Alright, there might be some other times, but they will be included for good reason.

I should say that both my short male nurse and Kanté's dad characters exited the story (true story) as quickly as they entered it. They rigged me up to a drip and then they were gone. The nurse had made a right old balls-up when it came to inserting the cannula but, to be fair to him, and Mr Kanté, they got there in the end, and I survived. Big thanks to those guys. Two of the many.

A doctor came to see me. I retold the whole story (pretty much) and whilst I talked, he prodded and pushed into my abdomen.

'Does this hurt?' he asked me.

'Not really – only because you're pushing.'

'And this?' he asked as he probed a new spot slightly lower and to my right.

It did hurt a bit.

'A bit, yes.'

'Has anybody examined your testicles today?'

Hang about, I thought. When asking me, the doctor laced his words with a suggestion of 'Please say yes', whilst at the same time knowing, in the absence of any notes or results, that the answer was going to be no. I'll state for the record that neither of us wanted what was about to happen, to happen.

'Er...no,' I replied. My voice must have hinted that there was nothing wrong that far down, so we could skip that particular test, couldn't we?

'Ah...' He paused. 'Then, is it alright if I examine you just to help us get to a diagnosis?'

Oh, for fuck sake. Come on then, let's get it over and done with. Worse things happen at sea – stiff upper lip and all that. But just the upper lip to be stiff today, I told my genitals in preparation. My dignity had truly taken the day off.

'Yes, that's OK.' I wasn't sure what would happen if I turned the guy down. Poor sod, I thought. My job wasn't all glamour, but at least I didn't have to play around with some stranger's knackers during a shift. I won't be too graphic, but between us, we made the best of an uncomfortable situation. He drew the curtains and I bravely pulled down my trackie bottoms and pants just enough to expose myself to him. I watched as he gently gave each testicle a squeeze and asked me if they had been painful or swollen. I told him they had been OK and with that inspection complete, I pulled my trousers and pants back up. My genitals seemed to be doing fine, thank you very much.

After writing a few notes the doctor looked up and said, 'We were thinking appendicitis, Philip, but you are not at an acute stage. This is why we are keeping you in for some tests and possibly we may need to operate so you won't be allowed to eat for the rest of the day.'

Now I'll pause there. That was *not* the moment when *Time Stopped.* That was to happen in about 19 hours. But, for someone that was a bit of a self-confessed pig, being told I wasn't allowed to eat was a massive issue. I had always been a fairly big guy – 15 and a half stone / 6 foot one – therefore my engine needed plenty of fuel. For a year I had been a really good boy and done my side of the bargain since that diabetes diagnosis I mentioned before. I'd done a bit of exercise on the treadmill and cut out snacks and generally lost a fair bit of weight – in fact, the most recent blood test results said I was below the threshold that they consider as diabetic but, the cloud to that particular silver lining was that I would always be considered diabetic similar to those people with asthma. I was a slightly trimmer pig, but I was still totally in love with my food.

Contrary to what food I enjoyed, at that particular moment, I actually didn't care. I had no appetite to speak of. I'd missed breakfast for the first time in a long time (probably since the last norovirus outbreak at home) and lunchtime had melted away with all the GP and A&E business. My stomach wasn't interested in food – instead, it told me in its own little way that it, and his associated intestines, was suffering and I should not complicate matters by eating anything – not even a Kit-Kat.

I hadn't taken in much in the way of fluids. After the spilled water episode, I might have had something from the second cup. Let's just say that I had a few sips during my staycation. It wasn't much more than that.

Hang on a minute. *Appendicitis? Operate? Keeping me in? Tests?* Seriously? Bloody hell. I could well do without any of that. Did he say appendicitis? Shouldn't I be doubled-up in pain?

'Appendicitis? Really?' I asked – not sure that asking the same doctor qualified as a second opinion.

'Maybe, maybe not. We're not 100% sure yet. We're going to get a CT scan sorted and we'll take some more blood tests. We'll start with getting some antibiotics into you and see how you respond.'

'Oh, OK...'

His questions continued. 'Are you allergic to penicillin?'

'Er, no...'

'Do you have any allergies?'

'Not that I know of.'

He seemed happy enough. I was left there. Just me, my drip, and my recently squeezed bollocks.

Within ten minutes, another nurse – this time a female – came over and asked me, yet again, to confirm my name, date of birth and if I was allergic to penicillin. Upon arrival, I had been tagged with a plastic bracelet with my name and a barcode like I was attending a Sandals all-inclusive resort. They could look at (or bleep) that bracelet, I thought, rather than keep asking me to confirm my birthday every two minutes. Before I knew it, another bag of solution had been hoisted up and connected to my cannula. Double bagged. Maybe it was two for the price of one Happy Hour. That, I think she said, was the antibiotics I had waited for. I lay back and looked up at both the bags. I watched each drip contained within the tube about a foot down from the bag. Two drips trickled through two tubes. One was slightly faster than the other. I had no idea why the speeds were different, and I never asked.

More Tests, More Confusion

Shit. The battery on my phone had got low.

Early panic had put his clothes on to start his shift. It was in the red at 11%. Not good. If my phone had been new, it might've been alright. But my old iPhone, when it was on a downer, really liked to die on me. I bolstered myself – there'd be no sodding deaths on my watch – not even my mobile. I needed to be economic with usage, which was going to frustrate the hell out of Ali as I couldn't just leave it on and be available. She would be in the dark in between my updates. What else could I do? If they were keeping me in overnight, I'd need a charger.

I sent a message to Ali to let her know about my battery problem and then I flagged down a nurse (or she might have been a nursing assistant) and asked if, by any chance, they had an iPhone charger.

'No. I'm sorry,' she said, 'but they might have one on the desk.' She turned and off she went.

I spent a few minutes and checked over the report the GP had handed me, and then the nurse came back to say there was a phone charger in the house, but she couldn't bring it to me, so I would have to trust my phone to her. I passed it over. My lifeline to Ali. I hated how reliant I had become with the bloody thing. An hour should do – just to get by. I could survive the next hour – of that, like Bing Crosby, I was certain.

ECG time. Otherwise known as an Electro-Cardiogram for those that didn't know. As part of all the numerous tests, they wanted to see how my dodgy chicken tikka was responding. Yet another nurse came by and stuck the stickiest pads possible to my wrists and to my ankles and, rather obviously, four places on my chest around my heart. I watched her do her thing and added to all the tubes, there were now several wires and cables that ran from the little probes in each sticky pad to the ECG machine – and it silently collated data that could have changed the course of the day's festivities.

As I waited, I looked back over the GP's report. Interesting read. Shame I barely understood it. I was doing myself a disservice there. I was not a complete idiot – I understood enough of it.

"Last two days increased urine frequency" – Despite a thousand wees in the night, I hadn't been for quite a while. Not for four or five hours, but once I'd read it...how annoying – the sheer power of suggestion meant that I needed to go for a wee, but I was plumbed into that sodding drip. OK, I thought - I would cross that bridge when I really needed it.

"Temperature" - Yeah, a bit of a temperature. Not raging as such, but the Covid police would certainly make me stay at home.

"Diabetic on Metformin (last Hba1c 39 June)" – That was what all the fuss was about. I was new to the diabetes game, but I seemed to be doing OK. They'd checked out my eyeballs, so I was OK with the going blind threat, and they prodded my toes so it seemed I'd be OK with the equally horrible foot amputation threat as well. The Metformin was a fairly minimal dose that allowed me to not worry too much about what I ate and the Hba1c referred to the glucose levels that showed up in my blood – '39' was at a level well under a diabetic diagnosis and that had only been taken a few weeks before.

"Not feeling well" – no comment. Although not out and out sick, I had wondered why there was so much attention. Must be the diabetes, I reminded myself.

"No photophobia, no neck stiffness" – No that didn't mean I had a fear of selfies. I refused to Google it, but I reckoned it meant they were satisfied that I didn't have an aversion to light. I didn't mention it before, but Dr Shabani shone a little pen light into each of my eyes. I assumed that's what it meant. Although my neck had felt stiff, I must have either said no to the stiffness question or I had moved my bonce from side to side with ease. I can't remember that part of the examination. It turned out that the doctor's tests were carried out to clear me of suspected meningitis.

"Alert and orientated" - How nice of the Doctor to throw in a compliment or two. We should all make a pact to be alert – the country needs more Lerts. 3/10 for that awful dad joke. Orientated clearly meant that I was the right way up and knew where I was.

"Pulse rate 105 beats/min – Tympanic temperature 38.8 degrees C – Peripheral oxygen saturation 98% - O/E blood pressure reading 124/77 mmHg – Blood glucose level 8.5 mmol/L".

There was a lot of information in that box. A lot of vitals for me to go through. Pulse over 100 looked worryingly fast to me. However, hospital was a terrific place to be if planning a cardiac arrest. Tympanic meant my eardrum, so logic would suggest that it had something to do with the special thermometer they had jammed into my earhole. What I did know was that the temperature was high. Not quite hitting the heights of over 40 degrees that Jayden reached a couple of years ago (we could laugh now how the cheap plastic strip thermometer shot through its rainbow of indicating colours when it came into contact with his forehead) but it was a concern, especially with everyone still banging on about Covid. 98% was OK when it came to oxygen. I wasn't sure what would constitute a bad result at the time but it told me at least my breathing and lungs were pulling their weight.

Blood pressure? Mmm, that always confused me. I could never remember which was the more important reading, but it looked like the first reading was high and the second one seemed really low. At the time, it didn't really register as I'd had my blood pressure done a couple of times since and nobody was rushing me through to the operating theatre for open heart surgery, so all good there as well.

Glucose at 8.5. No idea (because I was still a novice at the diabetes scoring, as I've already explained). It turned out that my score was perfectly normal so they couldn't have been worried that I was about to go into a hyper-glycaemic shock.

"Chest fairly clear" - Fairly? That sounded a bit vague. It was clear. A little bit hairy, but nothing to write home about.

"dS I+II+O" - I might not have got the first letter correct because the report was still drying out. Maybe it had something to do with blood. I knew I was O-positive from my history of blood donation. It was good to know for when they rushed me through to theatre...

"Abdo soft, non-tender, BS present" – That's exactly what the sheet said. My tummy was normal (no hard six-pack as noted) but I wasn't sure why the Doctor recorded that I was bullshitting her.

"RT < 2" - Nope, me neither...

"Urine infection but also diabetic on Metformin" - I guess that entry just confirmed exactly why I was lying there on a comfy hospital bed, taking the afternoon off work.

"Needs hospital review to check for sepsis and acidosis on Metformin. PW ambulatory care for Medics review in A+E and then they can review if he is well enough" - Oh. I read sepsis. That was one thing I *did* know about. That could sometimes be quite serious. In fact, it could kill. I had heard many horror stories of people that might have just had a simple cut to the hand and three days later they were dead. Sepsis. I hoped it wasn't that. I didn't want to be one of those horror stories. I considered whether I had suffered a cut recently. No. But I guess it wasn't as simple as that. Hypochondria, Early Panic's next door neighbour, had put his boots on and was ready for a determined stomp around my inner most thoughts. It had to be something and maybe my self-diagnosis of a urinary infection wasn't correct. Acidosis on Metformin – I made a stab in the dark that maybe it meant I was having some digestive reaction to my diabetes medication. I had no idea if acidosis was bad or relatively innocuous. The back half of the note about me being assessed in A&E had happened, although nobody had confirmed if I was well enough one way or the other.

The rest of the form at the bottom was full of phone numbers and NHS internal information.

It was the idea of sepsis that preyed on my fears the most from all that technical blurb. I felt the need to share it with Ali, but with no phone, I needed to get the attention of someone to claim my phone back. Hopefully there had been enough time to give it a boost and therefore enough battery to last for an hour or two. But before any of that – I really felt the need for a trip to the toilet.

Bugger. Things weren't going to be straight forward. Drips and ECG attached – no chance, not on my own anyway. I'd have to hold it in.

Based on what I'd heard from others and the experience I'd gone through with Harrison (my eldest), I resigned to being rigged up to the ECG for 24 hours at least. But no. I reckon I'd been attached for less than an hour when the ECG nurse came by. She lifted up the graph paper that had drawn out my pulse over the last hour or so and seemed pleased with results when I asked her if I'd passed the 'Lie Detector' machine. Not her call though, she needed to run everything through the doctors, but I wasn't to worry. She unplugged all her electrodes from me (picture that scene in The Matrix when Keanu broke loose) and I was free. Free to get to that wonderful toilet – I could almost feel the relief already.

The toilet wasn't too far away. Distance was not the issue. Luckily, it wasn't too busy in the ward and after checking in all directions, I was sure that it was vacant. Let's go for it, I decided. I shuffled my legs around to the side where the drips hung and then attempted to get off the bed. Obviously, I tried to land as gracefully as I could, but the gown had other ideas and decided it wanted to expose as much flesh as possible. Good job I had checked that the coast had been clear of prying eyes – the Paparazzi were nowhere to be seen, and anyway, up-skirting had recently been made a crime. At the same time to when my feet hit the floor, I beat down my gown back into place and I stood upright and proud next to my bed. Phase one complete.

Phase 2 involved the journey to the bathroom. It was relatively easy. The little wheeled drip trolley developed a life of its own and insisted on spinning clockwise as I coaxed it along with me. I did my best to conduct an anti-spin move on it, so the tubes didn't get too twisted, and it appeared to work. Then the door handle confronted me. I wasn't a germaphobe, but our dear hospitals always put me on edge. The previous 18 months had given us nothing but Covid this and Covid that, wear a face mask, sanitise hands blah, blah, blah, and all of that shit, so it really made me stop for a second because I saw a surface I didn't want to make contact with. I was in the hospital gown otherwise I would've pulled a long sleeve down to cover my hand.

Sod it.

After the dramatic pause, I used my bare hand and pushed the handle down, entered the toilet and dragged my reluctant contraption with me. I considered that maybe the raging sepsis in me could have a fight with the MRSA or some other Superbug that lurked in a place full of ill people's bodily fluids. And solids. And semi-solids...sorry, was that too much info?

Just go with it, I said to myself, *and thoroughly wash your hands after. Then sanitise them. Sterilise them. And then maybe sanitise them once more.*

And I promised not to lick my fingers for at least a week.

Don't judge me too harshly, but Phase 3 turned into a lady-like sit-down wee. After an examination a couple of years ago, I'd had it confirmed that my prostate had been growing nice and steadily over the years. They did some tests and they told me it wasn't cancer (phew), but that it was simply enlarged. So that very private gland of mine now sat within me like a big old coconut and caused my flow to be an unspectacular trickle, even when bursting for a wee. Don't worry, I had taken some toilet paper and given the seat a courtesy wipe first before I let my bum cheeks make contact with that unwanted plastic surface. I didn't hover – that was one step too far. I still felt bloated, and my guts were clearly not right, so I sat there for a while and hoped that I could encourage a satisfying poo to appear and clear all those troubles away. No dice, I'm sad to say. Still nothing moved down there. Oh no, what if I was suffering with a blocked bowel? I'd heard stories about it. It wasn't particularly nice to think about - shit being stuck inside. As the longest wee of the day came to an end, I consoled myself with the fact I was in the best possible place if my bowels were indeed jammed up.

Hang on, my dad had bowel cancer a few years ago...

It was perfectly normal to consider cancer every single time we ever felt unwell. The media constantly reminded people that 1 in 2 would get it. I dismissed it – I was happy to stick with my urinary/bladder infection diagnosis as I was still weeing and feeling feverish. I kept on saying to myself and anyone else prepared to listen, I wasn't feeling that bad.

I finished and found pulling up my pants and trackies with one hand to be another challenge as I didn't want to yank on all the tubes that came out of my left arm.

Oh great! The gown tie-ups that should have been double knotted around my waist had dangled themselves into the toilet bowl. Fucking marvellous. Just typical. I'd tried to keep everything as hygienic as possible, only to find I'd dipped my gown in the bog.

I shuffled to the sink and did my best to dry out the ends of the piss-soaked gown-ties by using up several paper towels. Then I discovered I was a little confused with the mixer tap. Using them was often down to pot luck. I could turn the chrome handle to the right, but how cold, tepid or scolding hot was down to how far I moved it. Or would lifting it up affect the temperature or just the power of the flow? I made the executive decision that I simply could not be bothered to wait for several minutes for the stream to get warm, so I turned the handle, and accepted the cold temperature I had been given. No drama. I used plenty of squirty soap and used three or four paper towels. There was a pedal on the bin, so I stamped on it to open it up, and threw my used-up towels in there. I let myself out by turning the snib lock on the door, thus completely infecting my hands with MRSA or whatever was stuck to the shitty door handle.

Strewth.

An Excursion to Break the Monotony

I sent a message to Ali.

She asked if I could have visitors.

No – because of Covid restrictions, that door was shut.

I told her I had just had my chest waxed as a result of the ECG because they'd used the stickiest rubber pads known to man. Ali confessed that she was paranoid that I had a tapeworm. I blamed John Hurt in *Alien* back in 1979 for putting the idea in my wife's head that some parasitic animals gestated and developed at lightning speed but she genuinely believed that I'd eaten some under-cooked food and a tapeworm had taken over my body. Nope, it wasn't a tapeworm. I let her know that the medication had kicked in, my temperature had come down a bit.

Surprisingly, Luigi from Mario Kart turned up next to the bed with a wheelchair instead of his green buggy. He had shaved off his moustache, changed his green dungarees for some blue hospital overalls, lost his hat and his European accent didn't sound Italian to me.

'Hello, Sir, are you ready to go for your scan?' he asked.

'Oh, OK. Sure,' I replied. 'I didn't have much else planned this afternoon.'

With his help, I managed to get into his wheelchair. The hardest part proved to be the untwisting of the tubes, but he managed to arrange the drips so that they were propped up on a pole behind me. And then off we raced. Luigi had a 'Manny' name badge on his shirt which, confused me. During our brief F1 qualifying session I found out his real name was Manuel and not Manny or Luigi.

'From Spain?' I enquired – which I believed was the more politically correct question rather than a Barcelona reference (although, I was ashamed to say, that question would have come next).

'No, Portugal,' he said. He was nice and friendly about it.

I remarked that he seemed to know the twists and turns of the corridors extremely well (the best racing line) and it turned out he'd been wheeling the infirm around the hospital for more than 30 years. Other staff members passed the other way and smiled (with their eyes – remember, it was face mask-wearing Covid times), or they waved and said 'Hi' to us as we whizzed on towards the scanning room. I felt I was in safe, fast, popular hands. I felt a little bit sad that Luigi (real name Manuel), like many in the building, was probably on minimum wage. I mentally gave him a 10/10 rating and with his gentle voice he announced that we had arrived at the doors to the scan room.

He went inside to let them know I had arrived, and I waited outside as the most patient of patients. His voice sounded friendly and reassuring. 'They are just finishing with someone but you're next. Shouldn't be too long.'

If he wasn't the best porter ever, he wasn't far off.

'Thank you,' I said.

Luigi was right. It wasn't long before the double doors opened. A hospital bed emerged slowly, pushed by another porter. I could just about make out an ancient human on board. A woman. She might have been dead. There was no movement, and her eyes were shut. There was nothing of her. I saw her head and short white hair, but there didn't seem to be much of a body between the sheet that covered her and the mattress. I wondered what was wrong. I imagined what they could've possibly scanned as there wasn't much body there. Maybe she had ended up there after a similar bout of constipation. Luigi and I barely moved as we watched the porter silently wheel the bed away.

A young nurse broke the moment when she came out of the same double doors. She looked down at her clipboard, then at me, and asked, 'Philip Honey?'

'Yes,' I responded and without further ado, Luigi handed me over and she wheeled me inside.

'Good luck!' Luigi called from behind me. 'I'll wait here for you.'

He was the best.

The CT Scan room looked beautifully spacious. Wexham (not Wrexham) Park Hospital, like pretty much every big town or city hospital, was old, ugly and dated. It had served the locals for many decades, but I figured it should be razed to the ground and a new, modern facility with a decent (free) car park could replace it. Everyone agreed. That, obviously, was not going to happen due to money, so like other, similar establishments, every now and then there was some refurbishment here and there or maybe a new wing or extension. The site had now turned into a mishmash of different looking buildings and bolted on wings that seemed to do its best to help keep people safe and well and alive. All three of my children entered our wonderful world through the time portal of my beautiful wife's birth canal and into the maternity ward at the hospital, so I felt some sort of attachment to it. The A&E department where I had ended up was all shiny and new in comparison with the rest of its departments. I guessed it to be 4 or 5 years old and therefore pretty modern. It made the experience for patients slightly more bearable, and the environment must have been a hundred times better for the staff, who had to spend most of their days there.

The first object I noticed was the imposing white machine positioned in the middle of the room. I wasn't sure if it was same monster that did MRIs, as I knew people that had experienced it and I noticed a flat bed for me to lie on and a big-looped part that the patient passed through where all the magic happened. At least it wasn't a big tubular coffin, it was open so if I became claustrophobic, I'd be OK, but that was as good as it got. To the right, I spied a little office with desks, monitors, and the CT operator, whilst still looking at his screen, gave me a brief 'Hi there.' And I returned the gesture.

He got up from his chair and joined me where I had been parked in front of the machine. Tall, dark and handsome. I reckon early thirties – I clocked the name badge that declared his name as Chiraq. Yes, he looked like a Chiraq. His assistant, armed with a clipboard, looked like his younger sister, and they felt like a solid team to me. She asked me the same questions everyone else had.

Date of birth, first line of my address, any allergies and then a new one...

'Have you had a scan before?'

'No. First time.'

'OK. Can you please complete this form for me?' she asked and then handed her clipboard to me.

There was some crazy shit going down on that form. Essentially it asked me if I was pregnant or had any history of having a reaction to radioactive dyes or iodine. Iodine? It brought me back to my days playing American Football on AstroTurf. My knees would suffer terrible burns from the plastic pitch and the physio guys loved spraying Iodine on the wounds. It used to sting like hell but, at the time, with adrenaline pumping through my veins, I didn't really care. Today, twenty years later, they were going to inject Iodine into me. Lovely.

My responses on the form looked fairly robust to me – apart from confirming diabetes and my Metformin medication, I reckon I was low-risk of having a heart attack during the process. Not that my professional opinion counted for anything. After signing it at the bottom, I handed the clipboard back to its true owner whilst Chiraq put a cuff around my bicep and took my blood pressure.

'This cannula will need to be changed, I'm afraid,' Chiraq told me.

Bollocks, I could well do without another performance of cannula fitting. 'What's wrong with this one?'

'Unfortunately, it isn't big enough for us.'

Marvellous. They had different sized cannulas. Well, you learn something new every day (or every few minutes in my strange day).

The blood pressure machine had done its job and Chiraq's sister noted the scores on the doors. She stumbled into my drip contraption and for a moment she gathered herself, but then she totally lost her balance and fell onto the vinyl floor. Luckily, she hadn't really hurt herself or yanked anything out of me.

Chiraq gave out a laugh – the fall was quite funny. 'You're more clumsy than me. And I'm the clumsiest person in the world!'

What?

'Hey!' I blurted. 'That is not the most reassuring thing to say when you're supposed to be looking after me.' I'd like to think my tone was jovial. It was time to keep the mood light.

'Oh! Sorry!' Chiraq laughed even louder. As did his little sister. 'I'm only clumsy when I'm not at work. Honest.'

'Yeah, OK. We'll see about that.'

From that point on Chiraq and his sister were the consummate professionals. To get ready for the machine, Chiraq's sister asked me to remove my shoes and to put anything metal to one side. I removed the white gold chain from my neck (finally, after 22 years) and my wedding ring (after nearly 23 years) and I removed my tracksuit bottoms as well. Luckily, I had some half-decent underpants on – always be prepared. Both my mum and cub scout master would be so pleased with me. I bundled all these belongings up and balanced them back onto the wheelchair and shuffled myself on to the bed part of the machine. A long piece of white paper towel acted as the bed sheet and I tried to caterpillar myself on the bed so that my head was on the cushioned bit.

Chiraq helped me get into the right place. He tied up a rubbery tourniquet just above my right elbow and asked me to make a fist and after several seconds we saw that a suitable vein had risen to the occasion.

I chose to look away and felt pleased that I had barely realised that the new cannula had been inserted and then expertly taped down. I hardly noticed that my blood had been taken either, and I felt as comfortable as I could be as he talked me through what would happen next.

'So, we are putting in an iodine dye into your bloodstream so that the machine can pick this up on the scan. You shouldn't feel anything as such, but you may experience a warm rush and you might think that you are wetting yourself, but this is perfectly normal and the sensation won't last too long. We will talk you through the process and it should take about 10 – 15 minutes and just listen out for the instructions when we ask you to breathe or to be still. Have you got any questions?'

For Christ's sake - I only came in for some antibiotics. That was a thought I did not say out loud. Instead, I said, 'No. No questions.'

They cracked on with their day job. It was getting towards the back end of Friday, so the working week was almost done. Not for the NHS heroes of course – they really were 24/7/365, but luckily for them we weren't in a leap year.

I didn't feel that ill. A bit tired maybe, and I had it in my mind that I could close my eyes and sleep through the scan. I was a cool customer, really I was. Unfortunately, they needed me awake to follow their instructions. They fired up the machinery. Chiraq got me to put my arms straight out past my head so they didn't get in the way of the picture, which wasn't the best sleeping position. I had to pull my gown up to expose my tummy. The tubes became a bit of a faff, to say the least, but eventually they were pulled into a safe place, away from the action. Chiraq and his assistant left the main room and dashed into their nearby recording studio, far from any harmful magnetic forces.

I heard a noisy hum begin and I could sense the machine gather momentum within itself. As much as I could claim to be cool, the buzz and acceleration and sheer power generated from the machine consumed all my thoughts. I'd never experienced anything like it before. I was physically exposed to the demands of the equipment and became frightened as to what it might detect deep within my vulnerable body. The process was painless, but the cannula nagged my arm and I was not comfortable. I felt I was in the centre of a massive gyroscope, and my whole world had become vibrations and noise and nothing else. I had become a slave to the power of the machine. I was at its mercy.

As the bed moved towards the whirring hoop that contained all the magnetic gubbings, I saw through a three-inch square gap and took note of the impressive speed of the revolutions within the large circle as it carried me deeper inside. It felt a little bit like how I would picture a futuristic cremation. No coffin, just vaporisation and no mess. Nice.

I moved on from the modern cremation idea and thought about 'The Jaunt'. Not many would know anything about 'The Jaunt' – a short story by Stephen King about the phenomena of effectively travelling through a time/space portal. While not a new concept, it has been written about and shown on the big and little screen many times over and I was a big fan of King because many of his stories were short and punchy, sweet and always memorable. According to the story, people had to be unconscious to attempt the jaunt, and without spoiling the storyline, it centred on the horrific effect the trip had on a young chap that enters the portal while he remained awake. I hadn't read that story in nearly thirty years but as I lay there, I imagined myself as the boy in the story – he, too, lay on a strangely futuristic bed, and found himself transported to an unknown destination, whilst remaining fully conscious. I hoped that, unlike the boy, I would not experience what an eternal journey was like, because Mr King hadn't painted a particularly pretty picture of it.

When my body was deep inside with my head poking out – no brain scans today – I felt the sensation that I was warned about. Something warm raced through my body. It was neither pleasant nor unpleasant. The rush probably wasn't intended to be nice, but I tried to be positive and likened it to what a good dose of Amyl Nitrate might do. I could only imagine. Now that they'd said it, I did get a bit of a feeling that I needed to wee, so I put extra effort into my groin muscles to make sure I didn't piss myself. Luckily the rush sensation only lasted a few seconds. As it faded away, an automated voice requested that I take a breath and hold it. There were some graphics in front of me on the side of The Hoop - one picture of a Pac-Man like head with the mouth open and another with the mouth closed and puffed cheeks. They lit up according to the instructions. I guessed they were for the benefit of young patients or maybe those that didn't understand or hear the language of the robot voice.

The closed mouth picture lit up and so I did what was expected and held my breath. Ten to fifteen seconds maybe. I suffered a minor panic because I had no idea how long I was supposed to hold my breath. A fear that the machine might have a fault also flashed into my thoughts. Then the other picture of Pac-Man lit and a female C-3PO asked me to breathe normally.

I exhaled.

As they predicted, the process took about 15 minutes. The bed glided me in and went out several times, and I breathed in and out as instructed. The big hoop whirred and hummed and took a few thousand pictures of my insides. The power of the machine was impressive and intimidating. If it hadn't been bolted down, I was sure that, with the centrifugal force generated, it would have lifted itself off the floor to then rampage around the scan room – then it would burst through a wall to demolish the entire hospital.

'All done,' announced Chiraq.

I wondered if he'd heard a microwave ping go off at his end.

'Are you OK?'

'Yes, thank you,' I said, truthful.

'OK. Let's get you dressed and then you're free to go.'

I climbed off the bed and put my trackie bottoms back on. I let the gown fall into place, slipped my feet into my trainers and put my chain around my neck. Good job I wasn't ill like the poor people that might have had to struggle to physically use the facilities.

I negotiated the tubes and drips as I got back into the wheelchair and thanked them both again. We all wished each other a great weekend and I was wheeled out to be reunited with Luigi.

'Off we go,' he joked. 'Next stop is X-ray.'

'X-ray?' I queried. 'Isn't all of this one big giant X-ray?'

'It says on my notes to take you for a chest X-ray. It isn't far. Are you OK?'

'Yes, I'm fine. I may as well get the full A&E experience. Let's go for it.'

We were back in Luigi's territory as we raced through the labyrinth of hospital corridors like Iodine dye pulsing through some poor bastard's vascular system. We exchanged greetings with others passing in the opposite direction, with a masked-up smile or a knowing nod. I'd lost all my bearings but Luigi knew the place like a colony ant knew his nest. I'd been to the X-ray department a few times in the past so I recognised it when we arrived. It was close to the old A&E ward, and he parked me to the side of the corridor to avoid causing a jam. There wasn't going to be a jam. It was now even later on Friday afternoon, and there was nobody else around. The desk was unattended. I hoped it hadn't been a wasted trip.

'Hold on,' Luigi said. 'I'll find someone.'

I did as I was told and held on whilst the super-efficient Luigi found someone. Luckily, despite the look of desertion, they were expecting me and the radiographer, with Luigi's help, wheeled me into one of the rooms and into position. I had to stand in front of the machine and press my chest up to plate. Both Luigi and the X-ray guy had buggered off and left me to battle with the radiation from the machine on my own. I was sure they knew exactly the measure of radiation to give a man of my size without turning me in to the Incredible Hulk. I rested my arms on top of the machine at shoulder level and read the word 'SIEMENS' in front of me. I smiled to myself as the branded word gave me some comfort. Why give me comfort? Why was a good question. It gave me comfort because Jayden, the reluctant driver, my middle child, had just recently secured an apprenticeship with Siemens in their finance division. Their company brand in front of me made me think of him and think of family. I'd be telling them all tomorrow about standing in front of the SIEMENS X-ray machine and how all their technology was saving our lives. I say saving – what I really meant is delaying my inevitable death for a little bit longer. That sounded depressing but that mentality sat perfectly fine with me. I don't know who first said, 'Good health is just the slowest rate of dying', but it was all right with me.

The truth was that something would get us in the end. But a huge 'Well done!' to all the doctors, nurses, surgeons and big conglomerate-healthcare-machine-making-companies for giving a lot of ill people some extra-time at the end of their particular game.

The machine took an X-ray of my chest area. It was all done and dusted in moments and I concluded that it was another test that was probably a waste of time but better safe than sorry, right? I once again verbalised my gratitude and was therefore free to go. Luigi had been waiting. The meter had been ticking over but, since it was the NHS, my new taxi bill was being split between me and the rest of the tax-paying people of our great nation.

After another contender for a track record, we screeched back to my almost-private corner back in A&E. Luigi helped me back on to the bed and untangled my tubing so the drips were nicely behind me. I'd been gone on my outing, inspecting and experiencing all the latest equipment, for a little while and what I really wanted to do was to find my phone and reconnect with Ali, let her know that I was OK and that they were really giving me the full works to reassure her that they really couldn't be doing any more for me. Unfortunately, the nurse that had taken my phone to charge was nowhere to be seen.

Eventually, I flagged down a different nurse who understood what I was talking about. Most of the staff used English as their second language, but after several attempts she grasped what I was trying to tell her and successfully tracked down my mobile. It was back to 34% which was good enough. It was incredible how stressful it had become, not having a phone or having a phone with a battery that was dying. I hated it.

Give me back the good old days.

I've Had Better Staycations

I called Ali and firstly reassured her that all was OK and gave her an update on the mini-adventure I'd been on. I told her the grim news that it was most likely that I would not get out that day and so I asked her to bring some bits and bobs in a bag. I didn't need much, and none of it was desperately urgent. My list consisted of:-

- Toothbrush, toothpaste, contact lenses, deodorant (whatever wash stuff could fit in an over-night wash bag)
- Glasses (in case my eyeballs rejected my contact lenses or vice versa)
- Phone charger
- Clean pants, socks and a T-shirt (trackie bottoms would be fine for tomorrow)
- My Metformin
- My Walter Payton book

Ali said she'd be up to drop all of that to me as soon as she had sorted the kids out, even if it meant just dropping it off at reception – I'd get the delivery no matter what. Thanks Ali. I love you.

A huddle of four doctors came to see me. The lady doctor seemed to be in charge and did all the talking. She asked me what had happened to me and I gave her my rehearsed speech. Then she asked if she could examine me.

'Of course,' I said. The more the merrier.

She was great. Confident and friendly, it seemed like she knew her stuff. As she felt around my tummy, she asked me if there was any pain.

'No.'

She pushed her fingers a little harder into my right-hand side – Hello Mr Appendix! 'And here?'

'A bit more there, yes,' I replied. 'Although I don't know if it is because you're putting extra pressure there anyway. I don't think I'm a classic case of appendicitis. I reckon I should be jumping off the bed with you pressing there.'

'Well, something like appendicitis has to start from some place and sometimes it can accelerate to cause us all a big problem. What we are going to do is keep you here overnight for observations and to see what all the blood tests and scans tell us. I can say that I've seen your chest X-ray and that seemed clear which is good news.'

She was about my age I reckon. In her fifties; she'd seen it all before.

'Oh OK. That sounds encouraging.'

'Yes. Although we haven't yet worked out why you've been so poorly but, hopefully we will get you some proper results soon.'

The chat was brief and to the point and she told me that they were soon going to evict me from A&E to the surgery ward. I was only allowed to sip on the water I had as there was a good chance that they could operate on me in the morning. Nil by Mouth. I still had no appetite so that wasn't a problem. It was the overnight stay. I really, really did not fancy that.

My weekend had gone tits up.

The Worst Sound I've Ever Heard

I was about to hear one of the worst sounds I'd ever heard.

I have a few sounds that are scarred deep into my memory. The crack of Chris Burton's shin bone (God bless his soul) six feet in front of me on a football pitch one Sunday morning was right up there, followed by his piercing scream two seconds later. Yeah, that was a horrible combination. If I did live long enough to unfortunately suffer from dementia, fingers crossed, I would be free of that blood-curdling two-tone sound. Silver linings and all that.

A&E had finally evicted me. I was on the move. My new bestie, Luigi the best-ever porter, was back with his wheels of steel and he chuckled as he told me I was his last fare of the day. Once more he helped me into the chair as we did our well-choreographed moves, which ensured I was tangle free. With hoisted drip bags and the few possessions I had with me settled on my lap, we escaped and raced to the ward nearest to the operating theatres.

Theatres. It's funny how operating rooms were called 'theatres'. Theatres were normally places to be entertained in, and maybe enjoy a song or at least a laugh or two. Operating theatres were at the polar opposite end of that particular fun-spectrum.

We reached a building I knew quite well. It was right next to the maternity ward. I may have mentioned it before that all three of my children were born at Wexham Park Hospital. All of them delivered in that very maternity ward. Positive, good vibes for sure. But we weren't stopping there.

There was a psychiatric ward next door, but apparently it was now dedicated to those going in or coming out of surgery. The hospital was forever changing. For most of the previous year, that part of the site, or at least the car park, had been operating as a Covid testing centre. Luigi reversed us into the lift and it ascended to the second floor, my new home.

The doors opened to floor two. And that is when I heard it - the guttural sound of the most painful grief. It all seemed so perfectly timed. I knew it was a female voice and I could tell that she was crying because the most loved person in her life had died. It was one of the most dreadful sounds anyone could bear. It wasn't a scream. It was pure grief.

It shook me.

I sat there, with a bleak sense of loneliness. Alone, except for the presence of that haunting wail. It grasped at my heart and squeezed out all happiness. The noise continued as long-drawn-out waves, and thoughts of death and loss washed over me. I couldn't prevent memories of the saddest events of my life. I recalled funerals I had attended for my cousin Paul and for my good friend Matt, both of whom died young, at around the forty-year mark. I hadn't felt sad for the boys themselves, they were gone, but what killed me was the sight of the mothers that were there to bury their sons. Auntie Viv found a strength I'd never witnessed before when she said goodbye to Paul, who'd died because of ill-health brought on after abusing his body for many years with alcohol and sleeping rough. I knew Viv had done all she could as a mother to drag Paul from his desperate situation. Then there was Wendy, who had shown me what a broken heart looked like after her son Matt had died from a motorbike accident in France. Matt was the first one from our gang to die. I was certain that her son's death triggered Wendy's health to spiral downwards, and fate took her life within a couple of years of Matt's tragic ending. The raw pain suffered by both women was visibly as immense as the love they possessed for their precious children.

The palpable emotion within the corridor where I sat seemed awfully familiar.

I felt that I had been wheeled into a ward of death and my hospital experience had suddenly become extremely serious. Grave was probably a better word than serious, as it really made me think about a hole in the ground and, ultimately, mortality. I did my best to stop thinking selfishly and considered what had happened to the poor woman that I could hear but not see.

Death.

Death, and the end product of grief that accompanied such an event, was our primal fear and the finite loss we felt, knowing we would never spend another second with a loved one, was unparalleled. The most powerful grief had a source deep within our core, our soul, and it radiated out, infecting everything that we were. It was a strange phenomenon, experiencing such frightening emotions that manifested themselves as physical pain. The sensation of guts being pulled in tight, the constriction of the throat, and organs in the chest actually hurting - the physical reactions that affected the noises that came out of the mouth.

I could tell that the cry had come from a woman in a state of maximum emotional pain. I could never replicate the sound unless it was at the precise time that I had just lost someone from my close family. I already felt vulnerable as I sat in a wheelchair with a potential operation to look forward to and even in my weakened condition, I instantly knew that the sound would be imbedded in my memory for a very long time.

Luigi wheeled me away from the lift, down the middle of the corridor and further towards the grief-stricken cry. It wasn't even loud, but it was loud enough, and it had a scary power. It had the power to be undeniable. It was raw and it was horrible.

There were a lot of people in that lift lobby and surrounding corridors. There was a significant Asian community in Slough and a good proportion of them seemed to be in that corridor. Mostly men, but not all, in every age range imaginable. Although I didn't want to look around and make any eye-contact with anyone, especially the crying woman, I had lifted my head up to see what was going on. Everyone seemed to be in traditional Muslim attire, and they spread out as best as they could with their backs to the walls and seemed to cover every spare inch so I couldn't tell what colour the walls had been painted. As the anguished cry continued, with the volume and tone paused only for breath to enable the distraught woman to continue to release her ultimate pain. The woman's extended family shuffled about slowly and moved just enough so that Luigi could park me up. I felt terrible. I was tired and off-colour, and the situation felt harrowing. Everyone else remained silent.

Ali and I had been so lucky; both sets of parents were still with us, yet many of our friends of the same generation had lost at least their mother or father. Some had lost both. A few had lost a partner; fewer still had suffered the loss of a child. Yes, we had been lucky, but we hadn't avoided tragedy. My own personal experiences had been called up from the back of my mind at the sound of the woman's cry. I'd been to the funerals of three of my four grandparents, but I was too young when my dad's dad, George, died. Terribly sad occasions and I, like the rest of the family, was emotionally drained by the end of it. More recently, I stood with my brother and read a eulogy at Gerry's funeral. Gerry had been my mother's partner for over twenty years and cancer had taken him away in less than year. There were a lot of tears on that day and obviously, before and after. Memories of Gerry distracted me – he had been so ill in his final days. I remembered my final visit to see him in hospital; it hurt to see him suffer, rigged up to receive the maximum amount of morphine possible, and a couple of days later – he was gone. Cancer. We don't get over the grief of losing someone close to us, someone that means so much.

Luigi whispered to me that he was leaving me there and was going off to find someone that would know exactly which room would be my destination. That was an exceptionally long two minutes, sat there grieving with the devasted family. I assumed it was the family's patriarch who had died, maybe an old, respected, wise man. I never found out who he was, how old he was or how he had died in that room. Very, very sad.

The ward sister bustled in to shoo the mob away. I sat and watched her crowd management skills. Because of Covid restrictions, there really wasn't supposed to be anyone there except maybe one relative. The family were not having any of it. She was firm, direct, polite and efficient and not one of them objected. I swear some of them were almost grateful that they had been excused from staying in that corridor, which doubled up as a portal to the afterlife. The men swayed and slowly shuffled down the stairs once they'd maxed out the 13-man lift. The howling continued and a couple of female relatives forcefully clung on to the crying woman/wife. Once the crowd had cleared, I glimpsed her through a tight bundle of three women.

Luigi returned to break the spell for me. 'We're in Bay 4!'

Thank heavens that I was leaving that area. Welcome to Level 2.

We made a few turns and I found myself at Bay 4 as predicted. I still heard the sound of grief, but at least there was distance between me and that heart-breaking scene. It was now mid-evening, sometime between six and seven, but because it was in the third week of June it was still sunny and warm and as we entered Bay 4, I noticed the wide series of windows in front of me that looked out over the hospital grounds below us. Bay 4 was quite intimate in size as there were only four beds.

All seemed quiet.

Yeah, too bloody quiet. I immediately thought the worst and assumed the residents of Bay 4 were either dead, or well on their way.

Bay Four

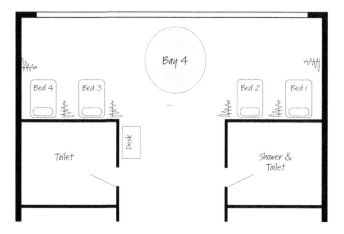

Luigi had slowed us down to a respectable, slow speed and he trundled me past an unmanned desk between beds 2 and 3 and then we made a left turn past bed 3. The curtains had been drawn at the sides of all the beds, but the end curtains were open so that when we rolled by, I caught my first look at my new roommate. It looked as though he was either asleep or a corpse. He lay on his back, eyes closed, with his mouth slightly open. In those few seconds I made out a man that looked as though he'd been in a car accident. He looked like he'd been scraped off the road, even though he was mostly covered with a bedsheet. Car or bike accident I reasoned - I could just tell by the face – I wasn't sure why or how. His hair was dark, quite short yet scruffy. He sported a fair amount of stubble (more than me) and his skin looked weathered, almost dirty, and I noticed some faded tattoos on the top part of his chest and arms that were exposed. I focussed on the grotesque arrangement of tubes that came out from his nose and were held in place with a mass of burgundy-coloured plasters. I don't know why I clocked the plasters so much, but they were the heavy-duty ones that when they were painfully removed, they took every last hair, a layer of skin and yet still managed to leave a mass of adhesive that couldn't be removed for a week, no matter how many showers taken. As we passed by, I spotted a bag fixed to the bed that collected the guy's urine. The bag looked quite full to me and quite dark. Like hangover-piss colour.

That'll be me tomorrow, I assumed.

A nurse, or maybe she was a healthcare assistant, had just finished making the bed. Bed 4 of Bay 4.

Luigi dropped me off and I said my thanks, waved him off and wished him a great weekend. He said he would see me later, but I don't think he meant it literally. We kept our voices down low so not to wake my sleeping neighbour.

I lay on top of the bed as it approached 7pm, but it was way off bedtime. The bed felt firm, which was good for me and my middle-aged back. The pillows were incredibly puffy and just using one felt that my head was at 90 degrees to where it should have been. I was used to super-flat pillows. I put my belongings on the clever tray-cum-trolley contraption that would prove useful for eating in bed. Whenever that was to be. After a few moments, before I'd even taken in my new surroundings, another nurse appeared from around the corner with a syringe in her hand.

By that point I didn't really care.

'This is to stop blood clots,' she told me after I had asked what else they were doing to me.

I found out that a daily injection of heparin (an anticoagulant) was a standard hospital procedure for patients that were not able to move about, especially after surgery, and therefore had a higher risk of developing blood clots. As if I didn't have enough to worry about.

'OK, go on then,' I relented.

She saw my cannula and a couple of taped on cotton wool pads in the crook of each elbow where bloods had been taken and she suggested I could take it in the leg if I preferred.

'Yes, please,' I responded, let the legs join in with the voodoo doll experiment. I felt it, but it didn't hurt as I think my skin had given up caring as well.

Left alone for a while, I had time to think about what had happened to me, where I was and what was going to happen. Everything felt so unknown. I hated it. I knew that there were hundreds of people in the hospital and, more than that, I had Ali, my family, and so many other friends to support me, just a phone call away – despite all that, I felt completely on my own. Loneliness. That was not nice to experience. The uncertainty of what they planned to do to me was stressful – I was in the surgery ward, but what operation were they about to land on me? I wondered if I was in a ward for lost causes. I feared that doubt, mixed with uncertainty, could harbour panic within me. I had a word with myself: *Stay cool, Phil – the last thing you need is for panic to show up.*

My senses were alert and yet they failed me. I could see everything around me, but I didn't have much of a clue what all the equipment was or what it was for. I could see the nurses hard at work and had seen other patients, but everyone was unfamiliar to me and I felt that human contact was strained and functional. I had tried to be upbeat and jokey, but it was hard to keep up the façade for any length of time. My ears were as useless as my eyes; they just confused me with overheard conversations filled with jargon I didn't understand. I could hear alarms in the distance, and I frequently heard a patient yell out in distress or pain – it all added up to baffle me, and I had a sensation of not feeling myself. I was totally unsettled. Panic lurked in the background, but anxiety brought on by the fear of the unknown, the uncertainty, and the loneliness seemed forever present.

My phone offered some relief and distraction from my anxiety, but there was only so much scrolling I could do. I had asked the nurse about visitors, and she said that it was too late that evening but I could arrange something for tomorrow. She gave me a small, laminated bit of paper that had a phone number on it. The Covid-friendly rules meant I could have one visitor for an hour between 11am and 4pm, but I needed them to phone the desk the day before and they would arrange it so that it co-ordinated with any other visitors to keep traffic evenly staggered. Unless I died, in which case my whole family could storm the building. I took a picture of the card and sent it to Ali. I told her that I had every intention of being home before the need for her to come and visit me, but could she at least bring a supply of essentials. The message came back - Oh yes, she certainly could! We were finally getting somewhere.

Ali had managed to make the all-important delivery I'd been longing for. The nurse gladly brought all the goodies over to me. Ali had asked me on the phone if I wanted her to bring all my painting gear to give me something to do.

'No, it's OK, wifey,' I had said, 'I can't be bothered with all the faffing about and the mess that would cause. Pelé can wait. I'll be back soon enough.'

Fortunately, Ali had been able to hunt down and bring the book I had almost finished reading, which was Walter Payton's Never Die Easy. I hardly ever read autobiographies – the truth was, I'd only ever finished Zlatan Ibrahimovic's book and the funny but not-really-a-true-autobiography from Alan Partridge, so it was a break from many books of fiction. I wouldn't expect many people in the UK knew about Payton's book, or that his nickname was Sweetness, but most people had heard of American Football. American Football, to the confused, looked like two rival motorcycle courier businesses were having a fight in the middle of a rugby match, officiated by WrestleMania referees employed to blow their whistles to stop the action at least every five seconds. It wasn't everyone's cup of char, but I absolutely loved it. When I fell in love with it back in the mid-1980's there was one man that stood out for me and that was Walter Payton. I was amazed by the way he ran with the ball. When a defender tackled him, and if he knew he couldn't dodge them, he'd put his head down and smash them out of the way. Walter Payton was the superstar role model that inspired me to play that ridiculous sport for ten tough seasons and I proudly wore the same number 34 shirt, and although I didn't run with the ball for 16,000 yards like Walter, I was quite proud of my little career.

Walter Payton died when he was 45 from an extremely rare liver disease. So, there I lay on my hospital bed, reading about how that great man (he achieved so much off the pitch) had died. Maybe it wasn't the kind of material I should have been reading, but what could I do? I'd read all about his glorious achievements, but the final chapters were all about the medical problems he went through and, ultimately, his death, his funeral, his family and his legacy. Nobody wanted to read about somebody dying in hospital.

Why had fate chosen a time for me to read about my sporting hero's rare illness just when I had become hospitalised with a mystery illness? Obviously, the crazy thought of coincidence crept into my thoughts. *Piss off*, I told that crazy thought, *just, piss right off*.

Walter Payton said, 'Never Die Easy'. Fight hard for every yard, every opportunity and even every breath – never give up. I knew I had a lot to live for, so I was happy to add weight behind that mantra, so I didn't plan on going down without a fight. God bless you, Sweetness.

When I'd felt I'd read enough, I put the book down and marked the page, even though I was nearly done, with the bookmark that my daughter, Lydia, had made for me. It symbolised a link to her, my beautiful, one and only daughter. She had made the bookmark for me in her woodwork class at school and after cutting out the main body of it from a sheet of thin wood, she had cut out the top part into the shape of an American Footballer. It's incredible how something so non-descript could equate to mean something so powerful just because someone I loved so much had thought about me. That was what that bookmark symbolised to me. I wouldn't get 50p for it at a Bargain Hunt auction but to me it meant the world. Properly priceless.

Without the distraction of the book, I was flooded with my immediate environment again. Noises from machines and more shouts from the ill. Someone, I could tell, was in a lot of pain. I was glad that I wasn't in any real pain. Yet.

I was a fish out of water, nothing felt *real*. I wondered if I'd actually left reality behind, for good.

With Friends Like These...
You Have to Laugh

I picked up my iPhone. The charger was clearly faulty but it was doing its best. If I angled it just so – it charged. If it moved half a millimetre, then it was hopeless. With the life it did have I exchanged messages with my brother, Richard, and also my close friends. I hated technology and the internet in particular, but even a cynical dinosaur like me could accept that it did have some good uses.

WhatsApping my friends got me through those troubling times in that hospital. I'd sent a few groups a selfie of a gowned-up me, face mask on with attached drips in view for added drama and I asked them: 'Guess where I am?' It became exhausting to catch up with the OMGs, the WTFs and the RIPs. That was the unfortunate problem of being so incredibly popular. Yeah, I wish. I recalled a selection of some of the more caring messages I received:

Richard: Whats wrong?? I have a mask just like that too...fyi

Sean: Worth knowing Rich

Richard: Have you caught Covid...you do live in Slough?

Sean: Maybe you can get a nurse to give you a wank

Richard: Fucking love you Sean xx

Sean: That's what happens in the hospital films I watch. Carry on Wanking

Richard: Hope its not sepsis...Helen's uncle got that in his foot...next minute...he's fucking copped it!

Sean: One foot in the grave

Richard: Septic meg

Richard: And don't laugh too much...you need to milk the hospital bed thing...rare as rocking horse shit

It seemed the more familiar the friendship, the more outrageous and offensive the (so called) support became.

My oldest group of friends included big brother Richard (we were always close enough to mix in the same friend group); Sean (Richard's best mate, but also my oldest friend); GaryMan (my best mate); and finally, Panda (the eldest and nominated Mum of our merry bunch). Since leaving school thirty-something years ago, we had done a tremendous job to keep in touch and to make the effort to go out every now and then to behave like naughty teenagers. At least I received more sensible concern shown in the texts from my old friends; Dangerous Dave, Tony P, Grantus Maximus and Spanish Javi. As the messages came in, I knew that both GaryMan and Panda were away on holiday (not together), so that spared me from even worse piss-taking.

I told my poker group the same story that I had been at the hospital since lunchtime and had ended up in the surgery ward waiting to see if my appendix would burst and try to kill me with a bacterial grenade. Messages came thick and fast from Jason, Brian, Pete, Pitt, Alexis and Rupert. That bunch of degenerate gamblers all wanted me back so they could win back their money. Or maybe they wanted to let me win some back; we'd played poker for so many years I'd truly lost track.

It had been a long day. Time had suddenly jumped to ten thirty and it was time to get ready for bed. The group stage of Euro 2020 had reached its conclusions, but that particular nightmare of a day was some sort of break day – could things get any worse? I resigned myself that there was no football to watch. I loved the Euros and especially the World Cup so I was pissed off that I could be missing out on a weekend bingeing on a glorious festival of football. That break in the tournament was a few days after Christian Eriksen had suffered a cardiac arrest on the pitch whilst playing for Denmark against Finland. I thought back to that remarkable time and how amazing the medical staff had been and how they managed to get his heart beating again after several minutes of officially being dead. That was scary to witness. The next match on the calendar - Denmark versus Wales - was not on until tomorrow. Still, it was something positive to look forward to.

With no football on, I took the washbag Ali had given me and trundled off to the communal bathroom situated at the start of Bay 4. I'd forgotten to ask Ali for a towel from home. No worries, I would use the half-sized, worn-out one provided at the 'Hotel Paradise'. The person that designed the bathroom had never, ever used it or tried it out. I wasn't going in for the full shower – it was simply a wee (still hoping for the all-clearing poo), the pinching out my contact lenses, a face wash and finally a brush of my teeth. Usual routine for me. Everything in the bathroom seemed so uncomfortable, clumsy and difficult. I laughed to myself, incredulous. The bathroom trip ended up being comic and horrible in equal measure. I'd anticipated the vinyl flooring so stayed in my trainers – no way would my bare feet make contact with that germ-infested surface. I didn't see anywhere to put my clothes, towel, or wash bag, except to balance it all on a plastic chair that I dragged out from the area near the shower. The drips attached to my arms and the gown - which I promised would be tied up properly once I spoke to the next nurse - hampered my movements. I became tangled and felt like Pinocchio before his strings were cut. The wash bag fell on the floor. I took out my disposable lenses and prayed my fingers were clean enough – a viral infection of the eyeballs was one of *the* most painful things ever to have happened to me. I tried to wash my face, but the tap and sink were so low it was tricky to either bend down and splash or stand up and carry the water in my hands to face. Both methods half-worked so I eventually got the desired effect. I dabbed my face with the towel and then came face to face with a dirty great pubic hair in the middle of all that whiteness. Simply marvellous. I gave it some respect as it was a classic shape with a long wavey stem and a tight curled up head and was jet black. It was like that moment in *Planes, Trains and Automobiles* when Steve Martin realised he'd been washing his face with John Candy's pants. Funny and disgusting in equal measure.

OK. Let's just get this performance over with.

Even the simple task of having a wash had become an ordeal. I was revolted with thoughts of germs. I was frustrated that nothing was in the right place or seemed familiar. I had got myself all worked up that my usual routine had totally gone to pot. I just wanted the sanctuary of my own bathroom. It was a form of homesickness that were uncharted (and parasite filled) waters for me.

I'd already accomplished a wee (the technique of swiping the whole gown to one side and gathering up the dangly ties had been truly mastered) so the home straight was simply to brush my teeth. Even though it was the 21st century, I didn't trust water from taps whether that was a place of work or even a five-star hotel unless there was a little sign above the tap that stated drinking water. Potable was the word. If there was a sign, I don't know why, but it felt even worse. So, I stood there and wished I'd brought some bottled water with me, but regardless, I would need a bit of liquid to get the toothpaste to work. Legionnaires' disease, Covid, MRSA or something worse might come out with the tap water, but what else could I do? I let the tap run for a bit - to clear all the germs that lurked, then flashed my brush into the stream. Minimal contact. I carried out my usual brushing routine and finished with a couple of spits. My dentist gave me a gum disease diagnosis last year so I made sure that I brushed the best as I could. Gum disease as well? It sounded like I was falling apart. I managed to change into some clean underpants and socks without any clothes hitting the floor, but the gown had to remain on. I got the ordeal over and done with and felt a little bit normal or at least a little bit cleaner.

I realised, at the tail end of my strange day, that I hadn't eaten anything. Luckily my appetite was alright with that. It had played ball and had not bothered me with hunger pangs or plagued me with cravings. As I skulked and shuffled back to my bed, I thought of the possibility of surgery, whether in the middle of the night or in the cold light of the morning, so the 'nil by mouth' was still relevant. No appetite – a rare event for me.

I passed the man, recovering in bed 3, as quietly as I could. He hadn't moved. I don't think he'd even opened his eyes in the few hours he'd been my neighbour. I had become a little more used to the technique of getting into my bed without getting too entangled with my two tubes. My bed happened to be completely flat with one pillow, unlike bed 3 that had been adjusted to lift the poorly man forward with at least two pillows. He even had his knees lifted – it looked really comfortable, and I wished I had the luxury of such an orthopaedic treat. I knew that I was going to have to sleep on my back and that it was going to be yet another challenge.

The lights had already been turned right down to allow those that wanted to attempt a sleep to go for it. I sent a last message to Ali to let her know I was planning on going to sleep, that I still felt OK and that I wouldn't call as I didn't want to wake up the guy next to me.

The message Ali sent back at 22:57 to inform me about a police incident fired me awake rather than settled me to sleep. She elaborated and told me how Jayden had got caught up in a violent attack at the take-away when he had tried to pick up some dinner for the family. He was fine but was a bit shaken after being intimidated enough to stay in the shop whilst the situation escalated and eventually, he witnessed the crazed intruder being over-powered by staff and other customers.

Jay was unharmed – the aggressor, not so. No one needed that kind of shit happening to loved ones at the best of times.

> Ali: OK. Got a police officer coming here in a minute for a witness statement. What a day.

Ali then asked me if they'd given me the CT scan results and I said that they hadn't. I knew nothing more than I had 6 hours ago...they still thought it was appendicitis, but weren't going to whip it out that night unless I took a serious turn for the worse. The messages continued:

> I actually feel sick in my stomach. No way will I sleep tonight. Just want you home snoring in my ear!

> I love you x

> Still love you more. Hurry home. Just doesn't feel right at all.

> Gonna try and get some sleep x
> If I hear anything more I'll let you know.

> Get some sleep. Let me know straight away once you know. Police officer here

> Of course x

10

First Night

It was time to end the chat and get some sleep. I had a standard-length phone charger, so it wasn't long enough to charge it and use it simultaneously. More importantly, because the charger was so dodgy, I spent several minutes to make sure the connection was perfect and I felt confident that the battery would be 100% in the morning, ready for a full day of keeping in touch with Ali and the rest of the world. Next up was the trial of achieving a decent amount of sleep to recharge my brain so I could equally connect with the world. Despite my mind buzzing with everything that had happened that day, and with the thoughts of what Saturday would bring (I had mentally prepared myself for an appendectomy), I reckoned I could park all that to one side and get some kip.

I was wrong.

If I could have moved into my usual sleeping position, I may have stood a faint chance. I, like everyone else in there, had to sleep on my back. A few reasons why – I had tubes connected to my veins, and every couple of hours, nurses came round and disturbed me to take observation tests such as blood pressure, temperature and oxygen saturation. And it seemed every hour they brought a new bag of saline to connect to my cannula, complete with cool flushes, together with the IV antibiotics.

Then there were the many trips to the bathroom, which meant I was in for a night of broken sleep. As a father-of-three, I've been well trained in the art of broken sleep. However, what kept me up most of the time was not the rigmarole of all the tests and the treatments, or the actual illness itself that raged throughout me, but the flashbacks I began to have from the last time I had to sleep at a hospital.

Almost ten years ago I spent a month at the very same Wexham Park Hospital. Not because I had been ill, but instead my son had been poorly. Ali and I learnt a lot during that dreadful time and one of the most important lessons I discovered was that the doctors, brilliant as they were, still had a great deal to learn. They might have thought they knew a hell of a lot, and they obviously did and they continually become better and better, but they certainly couldn't know it all. Up until then, I blindly thought they had everything covered, which was stupidly naïve of me. Of course, we didn't want those people to ever admit it, but there were notable gaps in their knowledge and there might be some illnesses or diseases that would never be truly understood or conquered. I would often say, 'You can't beat Mother Nature.'

Harrison spent a year suffering from the completely misunderstood Chronic Fatigue Syndrome when he was only a child of eleven, and despite the great attention of some superb doctors, we watched him deteriorate until he eventually had to be admitted to hospital. I stayed with him whilst he was there and slept on a fold-up camp bed next to him, then when the nurses woke us up at 7am I would have a routine of getting washed and dressed and then go to work and return later in the evening after Ali had done the late afternoon / early evening slot. It was truly horrible to find ourselves on first names terms with the staff. I had been so scared of how Harri's life would be affected by the illness. He was bedridden, permanently exhausted and was reliant on a wheelchair to have any chance to experience what other 11-year-olds did. That episode in our life was a book in itself, but a lot of what he and our family went through had been locked away and many experiences we simply don't remember. Our brains have banished memories of a lot of those traumatic experiences and for that I am grateful. Harri spent a year deteriorating, and then stayed in a terrible, barely existent state for another year – not getting worse, but there was no improvement either.

I remembered how, once I'd accepted my son was truly ill, I was racked with guilt and a sense of inadequacy for allowing it to happen to my child. How could I have let him down so badly? My job had been to protect him, at all costs, and the sense of failure had overwhelmed me. At his worst point, I was with him at the hospital, when Harri had a seizure of sorts. It was terrifying to witness. It seemed he was going through a kind of mental breakdown; his brain must have experienced the strangest surge of activity as he lay on his bed. Two nurses and I pinned him down and we had no idea how long the seizure would last. I saw his beautiful face contort into a grimace of sheer agony, tears spilled down his cheeks and with his teeth bared, he tried to hold back a continued groan so it never become the full volume scream that it threatened to be. It wasn't meant to be a joke to say that he looked like he was in labour.

Fortunately, the peak of that incident lasted no longer than a minute – a very long minute. I could only liken it to an electrical fuse board being subjected to a mass overload of power. I could visualise Harri's brain fire out impulses for all its worth. It was one of the most frightening minutes of my life.

After the electrical storm had passed, Harri became calm.

Utterly exhausted and with the help of sedation, the boy soon fell asleep.

Harrison woke up the next day and he showed a marked improvement. He barely remembered his seizure. I did though – I always would. Despite all my efforts to bury traumatic events in the backyard of my memories, that one would stick. I truly believed Harri's brain re-wired itself from that moment. The way his brain functioned, his thought processing, was altogether different after that episode.

Events and luck had turned a corner for Harri, and therefore the rest of the family. He took another year to respond to treatment and he recovered enough to go back to school and finish that distressing period of his life. It was not the best of times to witness a child being ill, pretty much every day, for three years. I thanked my lucky stars that we got him back, fighting fit.

I lay on my back and listened as machines beeped, alarms sounded, departmental phones rang with continual persistence, mixed in with the sounds of people as they moaned and called out – sleep did not claim me as quickly as it should have done. The memories and the emotions rose up from their graves within the depths of my memory; memories and emotions that wanted to stay buried.

Those emotions...of guilt for allowing my son to suffer for so long, the frustration at being powerless to help him; I had felt utterly inadequate, and probably still did. Those self-indulgent feelings were small fry compared to the larger spectres of raw fear and my feeling of hopelessness – they had been the worst enemies of them all.

I couldn't help but think back to those terrible times spent at the hospital with my son. The bastard known as fear had crept back into my thoughts, because it had been my turn to be in trouble. Fortunately, hope was still on my side, and he was alright. As long as hope stayed close by, I could remain sane. It upset me, exhuming old emotional trauma, but I had just enough rationality to remain positive for my own situation, after all, we did get Harri back from the brink.

11

Let the Vomiting Commence

The lights came back on. I could sense people moving about. I checked my newly charged phone and saw that it was 6:30am. Day 2 in Hotel Paradise had started up.

I had made it through the night then. Great stuff. If I added up the series of naps, I reckon I had about 2 hours kip at the most. *Be grateful Phil – it could have been worse.* It had been noisy, and I'd suffered untold interruptions, but I would be lying if I said I hadn't slept at all. People say they haven't slept when they've had a new baby. But they do, because it's just broken sleep and there was a massive difference between that and no sleep at all.

I checked the app for my FitBit. I'd been wearing Ali's FitBit for three or four weeks since I had a day or two of a noticeable, racing pulse. Jeez – I must have seemed like a hypochondriac. It was something (the palpitations, that is) that came and went. I wasn't particularly worried at the time but I kept the FitBit on my wrist just to simply do a monitoring role. Ali had actually sent me a message the day before to ask if I thought the illness was anything connected to my heartbeat inconsistency. I said that I didn't think it was. When it came to getting information out of the FitBit, I never did enough exercise to get excited about (I'll admit that most days I didn't hit the magical 10,000 steps) and all I ever really looked at was my sleep patterns.

My illness had broken the app. Apparently, rather than sleeping, I had spent the entire night exercising. Throughout the night my pulse had fluctuated between 95 and 120 beats per minute and classified 1 hour 49 minutes of 'fat burn'.

I sent a message to Ali to let her know I had survived the night and she sent me some kisses and ordered me to get some rest. The nurse that had finished off her nightshift just as I had got up told me that the doctors usually did their rounds between 9 and 10am so I had just a few more hours to endure before I found out how the experts thought I was doing and what the plan was. I passed on the information to my loving wife and gave her the impression that there would be no update for a while.

Although it only felt like a few hours between the trips, I made the effort to go back to the bathroom, went for a wee (no sign of anything solid but still a sensation of constipation) and washed myself to try and feel normal. The gown had been incredibly uncomfortable because I had sweated a lot during the night. It was heavy and damp, but I felt obliged to keep it on as I expected a trip to the operating theatre at any time.

On my return to my bed, I glanced over at the ill man in Bed 3. He seemed awake but only just. I thought his eyes opened slightly and I gave a friendly nod and the hint of a smile (face masks seemed to be optional for patients that moved around and I had chosen to go maskless).

'Morning,' I said, and not expected anything back. 'You OK?'

He had been propped a bit more upright by the nurses and it looked like he returned the nod but not the smile. I think he said, 'Yeah.' But it was more of a growl, like the sound someone made who hadn't spoken or used their voice in a year. He still looked terrible, but the flicker of life had to be a good sign.

'You look better than you did last night.'

He didn't say a word, but he nodded and looked directly at me. That was the extent of that first conversation and I felt pleased that I had given a desperate soul some encouragement that he would make it. His feet poked from the end of his bed and I noticed that he wore socks, both of which had huge holes in them, and I could see the entire sole of his right foot and all the toes of his left. I wondered if the poor man was homeless.

I returned to my bed and settled down with my book, but I sensed the hustle of the Breakfast Lady during her rounds. I overheard her ask the other cellmates if they wanted tea or coffee. I don't think the guy next door gave a reply, but I heard the lady call him Michael several times to get a response. He appeared to drift in and out of sleep or consciousness. At least I could now refer to him as Michael rather than 'the ill dude next door'.

The Breakfast Lady had obviously been briefed about me – the new arrival.

'Would you like some water?' she asked me in a soft, quiet way.

'Yes please,' I replied.

She pointed to the notice board above my bed and confirmed what I already knew. 'They are not letting you have any breakfast this morning. Sorry.'

'That's OK. Thank you anyway.' I was OK because I still didn't feel any appetite. It was well over 24 hours, maybe even 36 hours since my last meal - that kebab. In fact, if anything, I actually felt a bit sick.

'Do you want to order something for lunch or for dinner?' she asked as she handed me two different coloured menus. I didn't really know what the deal was at that particular all-inclusive, but apparently patients could order their chosen delicacies in advance, which were delivered to the bedside at the regimented time.

'Not just yet,' I confirmed. 'I'll take a look later. Thank you.'

She seemed satisfied with that response, took a jug of water from her trolley, and placed it next to my plastic cup on my bedside trolley/tray, then gave me a parting nod (and maybe a smile behind her facemask) and left me there with my book and my ever-increasing nausea.

I had been rigged up to a new bag of antibiotics and yet the feeling of nausea began to get to me. It seemed misplaced as I'd already endured quite a few hours of feeling awful. Whenever I'd experienced food poisoning or a sickness bug in the past, the vomiting usually made an early appearance, so it felt different. My stomach must have been empty anyway, which puzzled me. I needed to take my mind off such a disturbing topic because the thoughts of being sick could make people actually puke. I continued to read my book about my sports hero's death and did some browsing and messaging on my phone. The distraction helped.

For about thirty minutes.

The sickness refused to be denied and after it had lurked in the darkness for long enough, it finally took control of my body. The sensation felt over-powering and all too familiar and I accepted that it was not going to be choked back or swallowed down. I looked around for something to be sick in. There was nothing. I wanted one of the cardboard recycled bowls (no, they were not party hats) as I had seen loads of them about but, could not see any of them in my desperate moment of need. I pressed my 'Help' button at the bedhead – I urgently needed a nurse to get me some sort of bowl before the situation turned messy.

My throat did its own thing and became nicely wet, which made me swallow loads of saliva and mucus ready for the upcoming show. In my distress, I found my stomach grumbled and gave me the signs that all was not good. I felt my stomach cramp up, and the gripes had become more like a pain. The discomfort from the violent muscle spasms had made me feel even more nauseous – I had been sucked into a vicious circle, and there was only one way out.

Bollocks. The pain was too familiar – they were the contractions I had experienced many times before. I had no control over what happened inside my body, as the spasms started, and I doubled over, half-believing that if I made an external force to squash myself back into my tummy, it might counter-act the forces within. Nope. I rocked back and forth in a sitting position but that was futile, and I felt another wave of convulsions take hold.

I swallowed several times. The saliva and mucus in my mouth kept replenishing its stock no matter how many times I swallowed it. I let out an involuntary cough which was quite raspy, almost croup-like.

Fuck, that was close – that cough almost had puke attached to it.

My stomach reacted to the mouthfuls of spit I'd swallowed by going into another spasm that would have shot out sick had I not been fighting my hardest against the tide. It was painful and I was getting tired from the fight against the inevitable.

Where was that nurse? My little light stayed on to let anyone who happened to be around that I needed some assistance. I felt the cold sweat break out on my face, on my back...maybe all over me.

I got off the bed without any further plan of direction – I just hoped that being vertical might help. Nothing helped, not even gravity. I thought about sitting back down again. I had reached into panic mode. The taste in my mouth had changed. I could smell the juices in my stomach as they rose up from the acidic bag they'd been mixing themselves in.

More sweat, more spit, more spasms.

A coolness came over my face; I figured the blood had been redirected to my core – my hands, and no doubt my face, went white – yep, here it comes. Only a miracle could've helped me.

I accepted that the help requested might not be coming anytime soon. My thoughts consumed me. *Shit, I'm going to be sick.* Nothing could stop the runaway puke train. Being connected to the drip was going to restrict a dash to the toilet, and the truth was that I knew I only had seconds to spare. I had no idea how much volume would come up but there was no way the little plastic cup on my bedside tray would be a suitable vessel.

Over by the window! I finally located my only viable option - a basin that nobody ever seemed to use.

Well, that was about to change.

With one swift movement, I pulled the wheeled drip stand over to the basin. With fractions of a moment to spare, I performed some sort of semi-crouch and after another couple of successful preventative swallows, the gagging sensations overcame me, and I let it all happen – I needed the relief from the other side of vomiting.

I puked good and hard– it was noisy, painful, and it stank.

The convulsions brought up only a modest amount of watery bile. My stomach did a fantastic job to squeeze out every drop. I barked out textbook puking sounds to anyone within earshot. I did five pukes in total. Number two barely looked like a cup load, while three, four and five turned into painful and equally noisy dry heaves.

The relief I had anticipated and relied upon became real. My breathing returned to normal. Out of disgust, I spat out some saliva into the messy, ruined basin, and then spat out some more as I steadied myself and enjoyed the post vomit recovery phase. I turned on the tap and did my best to clear up the mess as my body returned to normal.

A nurse, or possibly a Healthcare Assistant, appeared by my side armed with a disposable bowl made of recycled card.

You're too late, I thought, as I looked up and gasped, 'I'm sorry. I didn't know where else to go. Sorry.'

'That's OK,' she said, and her voice sounded sympathetic. 'We can clean that.'

I had done well with the clean-up, although I had basically used the tap water and my bare hands to encourage the phlegmy bile down the plughole. It would need bleach or disinfectant for a deep clean, but I did my best and washed my hands and my face with the liquid soap located on the basin. I used several paper towels and trod on the bar at the foot of the neighbouring pedal bin and gave them a suitable send off as I chucked them inside and let the lid clang shut.

Thank fuck that ordeal was all over.

Relived and slightly exhausted, I took the shuffle of shame back to my bed. The half-dead guy had seen the show.

I apologised. 'I'm really sorry you had to witness that.'

'That's alright, mate,' Michael growled with his smoker's voice. I say growled only because it sounded like a gruff, gravelly voice, other than that it was friendly and genuine enough. It had to be difficult to speak properly with that horrible plastic tube shoved into his nose and down his throat. I hoped that I would never have that restrictive displeasure.

I got into bed and felt a lot better than when I had left it a couple of minutes prior. That's when I noticed that my bed did have a fancy remote control attached to it, after all. I then realised that I could push some of the buttons and my bed, which would mechanically tilt and move in hundreds of different combinations. They should have given newbies like me a proper induction upon arrival to Hotel Paradise. I thought maybe that could go down on my feedback questionnaire – assuming I would one day leave the bloody place. I played around with bed settings for about ten minutes until I concluded that I would never be comfortable for more than two minutes as I was in a significant state of agitation.

They cleaned the defiled sink. They checked up on me. I was OK, thanks. They had to put up with all kinds of horrible shit. They really were angels.

I let Ali know of my recent development. She would've wanted to know even though there was sweet FA that she could do about it. Except worry of course, because she was perfectly able, stuck at home, to worry herself silly about me. Like me, she just wanted to know what was wrong and what they were going to do to help me.

Soon after I'd emptied my guts, they had begun to serve breakfast. I was not envious. My appetite had not returned. I noticed that Michael was being encouraged to eat. He used his gravelly voice and chose a bowl of Rice Krispies and a yoghurt but no tea or coffee. He was not so dead as it turned out. He was going to make it and that positive feeling gave me a little lift. If *he* could come back from the brink, then there was hope for all of us – including me. I listened to the clank of Michael's spoon on his bowl (and then the metal spoon hitting his teeth). The process was slow and measured.

Bless him, it had clearly been an effort. I wanted to say something like, 'Go on matey!' but I opted to just let the man feed himself undisturbed. At least my puking hadn't completely put him off his brekkie.

Doctor's Rounds

I had been given new bags of antibiotics and saline before the doctors came around. They were all I was allowed for my breakfast. It was nearing 10am and the huddle of doctors were in with Michael. They had swished the curtains around themselves, but I still heard most of what was said. Only a weird person would not try to listen in.

The team of doctors (three or four of them) talked about Michael as if he wasn't lying there in front of them. I heard that Michael had come in for surgery on Thursday (the day before me, I presumed) and he had undergone some sort of stomach surgery and they were telling each other that the procedure had been successful and they were now monitoring his recovery. They occasionally asked him some questions, but I couldn't make out his quiet grunts other than he seemed to give them positive vibes about his recovery and how he felt. They checked out all the bags of liquids that fed him and one of them (I assume the junior doctor) was asked to record all the volumes and to take some samples. They asked him if he had eaten anything and he replied that he had eaten some Rice Krispies. They said that was a good sign and that they would like him to stick to a diet of soft food and to drink water for the next 24 hours. It went a bit silent whilst they checked his wounds from the surgery. The head doctor, who did most of the talking, asked the nurse to change Michael's dressings. After asking him how he felt, they asked him if he smoked and if he drank alcohol. Michael said he didn't drink and that he had given up smoking because it was bad for him. I didn't believe a word of it and I wondered why they had even asked him. Maybe I shouldn't be so judgemental, but Michael appeared the epitome of someone who had ended up in hospital precisely because of ill health caused by excessive smoking and drinking. It would have been generous of me to give him the benefit of doubt with regards to illegal drug taking, but I wouldn't have fallen out of that orthopaedic NHS bed if I'd found out he was into that particular vice as well.

The doctors continued with their questioning. 'Are you in any pain? Are you allergic to paracetamol?'

The head honcho confirmed that they would be sending someone from physio around later as it would help his recovery if he could get out of bed and move about. They said their goodbyes to Michael and I prepared myself as it was to be my turn next.

Whilst I listened in, I wondered what my fate would be. Rather than thoughts of *will I have an early morning operation and be home in time for tea?* – I had silly thoughts like – *Do I call them all Doctor? Do I not speak, and let them do all the talking? Is the slit in my gown revealing my privates?*

As much as I wanted to make light of everything, I also did dwell over big important issues like - *have I got sepsis? There were always risks when having any general anaesthetic, right?* Mostly I feared that the next conversation I was about to have might be all about my new colostomy bag.

The Time Bomb

I was on the bed but had adjusted the pillows so I was upright and alert for the huddle. There were four of them. Two men and two women.

'Hello Philip,' Mr D'Freitas began, 'how are you feeling?' He spoke with quite a strong Indian accent to match his appearance, despite the Brazilian sounding name.

I could understand him well enough even if the facemask muffled his words. I was honest with my reply, 'I would say not too bad, but I was sick a little while ago. I'm not sure if they told you that.'

'Yes. We have that. And now?'

It had been brewing again. The nausea. It had been all quiet on the Western Front for a while since, but I sensed the sickness desired a repeat performance whilst the doctors where next door with Michael. Now that I had been asked, I had to really question myself and that let in the notion that things were not as over as I wanted them to be. My breathing deepened.

'Not great.'

Bollocks. I felt the sweat as it prickled out from random pores all over me. Fuck, it's going to happen again. I just needed the lot of them to do their job and fuck off. I took hold of the recycled card bowl that was nearby.

'Ah. Well, Philip, I'm Mr D'Freitas and I'm with the GI Team here at Wexham Park.' He didn't introduce the other two doctors (who seemed junior) or the nurse (who seemed senior) but they all seemed friendly and smiley. 'We are responsible for all matters in the digestive tract from the stomach and all the way through the colon. Some of the tests are showing us that we do not think you have appendicitis and the scans are telling us that your colon seems clear and there are no signs of blockage or anything like that....'

My sickness did not give a flying fuck about D'Freitas' speech. I had to intervene.

'Sorry,' I interrupted, 'I think I might be sick again.' I got down from the bed. Some inner voice made me move position and I got down on my hands and knees in front of them with the bowl positioned below my face. Whilst the doctor continued, I rocked back and forth – sitting upright for a few moments then back on to my hands again. It was hard to concentrate on the news that came from the doctor's voice up high to my left....

'...ah...yes, Philip. OK...we haven't located exactly where your infection is but the antibiotics you have been given should be strong enough to work in a shotgun approach. Therefore, the plan is to keep giving you this until everything is back under control. Your blood tests have shown a very high white blood cell count and it should start to come down soon. We will need to take some more blood tests to monitor the situation....'

*That's lovely, now please piss off and let me honk my guts up...*I thought, or at least I was almost certain that those words did not leave my lips.

D'Freitas continued, 'However, we are going to need to keep you here for a bit longer as we do need to carry out some more tests as a result of what we found on the CT Scan yesterday...'

I interrupted his speech again, 'Hurrrr-Arrrrrrgggghhhhhhhhh.'

It was a dry heave. My stomach cramped and filled me with excruciating pain. Despite practically being an empty bag of acid-producing muscle, it did its best to turn inside out and squeezed a teaspoon of bile up my throat and into the outside world in front of the gathered professional crowd.

'...urrrrrrrrNnnnnnnnghghg....nnnnyYarrrrh.' I brought up an even smaller amount of luminous yellowy green bile into the bowl. I spat a few times to clear my mouth.

'...and what we found is that you have a neuroendocrine lump on your pancreas that we need to...'

Another contraction made me grunt (or bark) out loud yet again and, fortunately, no further liquids made an appearance because the nausea seemed to lose interest fairly quickly. Maybe it was the lack of volume of puke that was certainly not directly proportional to the volume of the puking sounds I made.

Sickness, you've done your thing – so now you can move on.

WOAH COWBOY!

I felt like someone (me) had stood on the brakes of the Express Train called TIME. I was braking with all my might... Fucking stop right there.

Stop. Fucking STOP! STOP!

Time, for the first time, did what it was fucking told and it did indeed stop. No one else would have noticed that event back in June, but I remember time had stopped - vividly.

Whilst still on my hands and knees I cranked my head up and to the left to meet D'Freitas' eyes. I thought I may as well square up to the man that had just announced that I would be dying soon of pancreatic cancer. I always wondered what would eventually get me. Maybe I was delirious with the sickness...but without being melodramatic. I wasn't sure what neuroendocrine meant, but it sounded something to do with enzymes and digestion according to my long-ago A-Level Biology studies.

'A lump?' I asked as I looked up at him.

'Yes,' he confirmed.

I broke eye contact and spat again into my bowl. It was a small cocktail made of bile, phlegm, mucus, saliva and some angry disbelief. It was all slimy and stringy and I needed the back of my hand to help clear the remnants from my lips.

On all fours, I must have looked like an animal. I craned round to look at him again for my next question. 'On my pancreas?'

'Yes,' he repeated. Dead pan.

Absolutely marvellous. *Ali is going to fucking kill me*, I thought, as I gave out a final defiant spit into the bowl.

I could not deny Time any longer. It gently started up again. Go on then Time – just keep creeping along, you ancient bastard.

I was almost grateful that Time had given me a moment in all those billions of years to at least acknowledge the importance of what was happening to little old me.

I let D'Freitas carry on with my death sentence. I didn't need to Google what pancreatic cancer was all about. I already knew it was the worst of the cancers with regards to mortality. As someone that had played a lot of poker, I was pretty good at working out the odds. Five percent chance of survival is what I calculated during that Saturday morning speech. All my chips in the middle of the table, cards turned over, all exposed with the betting done and I was sitting there, Heads-Up against The Grim Reaper...massively behind...but I had one card to come that could save me, just one magic card that could gift me a lucky, out-of-nowhere win. A one-outer we call it. I've seen it.... but they are (obviously) very, very rare.

Mr D'Freitas continued. 'I should also say that it seems to be on the tail-end of the pancreas which is encouraging and better than if it were the head, even if this is more rare. We will need to carry out some more tests like an endoscopy and a biopsy to see if there is anything else that we need to be concerned about so, I'm afraid, you won't be going home today. It appears to have grown into your spleen and the vessels surrounding this and we need to make sure that other organs are not affected. Once we have all the results in this goes to the Multi-Discipline Team review and then they will be best placed to tell you what treatment will be best for you. We may have to transfer you to Hammersmith Hospital as they are the experts with regards to the pancreas. I am sure you have a lot of questions so please ask anyone from the team here. The Macmillan nurse should be about this afternoon, even though it is the weekend, so we will ask her to check on you and see if you have any questions.'

I heard it all and I struggled up from the floor and slowly got back on to the bed. I say I heard it all, but what registered was a series of simple bullet points:

- Scan (we searched for **cancer**)
- Lump (**cancer** found)
- Pancreas (worst place for **cancer**)
- Rare (complicated **cancer**, in the worst place for **cancer**)
- Spleen (**cancer** is taking that fucker as well)
- Other organs (**cancer** spread)
- Biopsy (**cancer** confirmation)
- Treatment (worse than **cancer**)
- Hammersmith (**cancer** hospital)
- Multi-Disciplinary Team (serious **cancer** specialists)
- Macmillan (immediate help with my imminent death, from **FUCKING CANCER**)

Everything seemed extremely matter of fact and every element of the list was surrounded by dozens of questions all laced with dread. I wasn't sure of how to behave. It seemed that shock and denial had become my best friends at that precise moment. I sat on the bed with my legs dangling. Despite the devastating news I no longer felt sick. It was a strange sensation for me. I felt alert yet bedazzled. My brain was in a flat spin and yet I felt as though I understood what I was being told and in a weird way, I felt calm and in control.

Mr D'Freitas seemed stoic and firm.

As I gathered my composure, I could not believe that he had delivered such a serious diagnosis (or was that a prognosis?) whilst I was being sick into a bowl on the floor on my hands and knees like a fricking dog. Maybe he didn't have the time to come back later after I had finished puking my guts up. Nobody else had said, 'Maybe we should come back in 5 minutes…'

What a horrible way to hear such awful news.

The junior doctor looked the same age as Harrison – early twenties, and I could tell from her eyes that she felt uncomfortable about how it had all panned out. The nurse (who had obviously seen much worse, many times over) radiated efficient caring and unconditional support and the other doctor hadn't made eye contact with me as he had his head buried into his folder, frantically writing up notes.

Everything was so fucked up.

'How long will I be kept in hospital?' I was overcome with the powerful feeling that I just wanted to be home. I didn't care or think about much else.

I had to see Ali – hold Ali in my arms – speak to Ali – see my family. I had to get off that path to hell. In those first few minutes I felt overcome with the desperate need to be surrounded with my loved ones. I'd never felt quite so alone. I wanted to see my children. I needed my family. Time was now back on with his march to oblivion, so every second, every moment, had suddenly become precious.

Tell me that I can at least see my family.

'Well, at least a few more days. We need to see how you are responding to the medication and there will be other tests to do either here or at Hammersmith. The MDT meeting will not happen until Wednesday as they only get all the departments together once a week to discuss cases that cross over different departments and they will need some time to look at any results from the tests they will need.'

Desperately disappointed, I accepted it with a nod. I wasn't in a position to challenge it. As frantic as I was to see Ali and the kids I also knew (shock and denial left the door slightly ajar to let in some rational thinking) that shouting and screaming was not the way forward. My ordeal appeared to have grown worse by the hour, but I still had the weapons of a cool head and good manners. I also had private healthcare in my armour – they'd have me moved to plush surroundings, get me all tested and I'd be home for Sunday lunch. Yeah, OK. As I said, I accepted all of it with a slow, courteous nod.

There were too many questions that swam around my brain. Each one seemed more important than the other and therefore I couldn't actually ask any of them.

'I'm sorry I can't give you better news this morning, Philip, but I will see you tomorrow. If you need anything the team are here for you.' Mr D'Freitas gestured towards the chief nurse with the kind eyes.

'OK, thank you,' I replied, sombre.

They left me. I heard a 'Take care', a 'See you later' and maybe a 'Bye.' They probably didn't enjoy that morning delivery. I know I didn't.

I used the control panel to make the bed flatter. I pulled my feet up and turned so I could lie down. I stayed there for several minutes and played the scene over in my head. It was a strange sensation of numbness, disbelief and shock.

Fuck. How on Earth could I possibly tell my wife what had just happened? Christmas was six months away and I doubted if I was going to make it. The odds were not good.

Why me? Why fucking now?

What I felt was way beyond fear – I'd flown way past death, and I wasn't sure of what to feel about the blackness of oblivion that lived beyond death. Maybe because I'd never had to consider it before, but I wasn't scared of nothingness.

Well, not until that moment.

The truth was that I had been smashed. Devasted. So destroyed in every sense that I didn't have any strength to summon up anger.

I had always really loved a big family Christmas – I accepted that I would not be in attendance that year, or any others. What a fucking shame.

The Call

I never imagined that I would have ever had to make such a horrible, dreadful phone call to someone that I loved.

Despite it being one of the most significant conversations in my life, I can't remember the exact words that we used to each other. In my defence, I was still in a flat spin, but what I discovered was that I had a superb coping mechanism. Well, it was something that worked for me, yet plenty of others, like Ali, find the exact opposite works for them. In those 10 minutes or so, before I picked up my phone, I had a moment to add up everything Mr. D'Freitas had said to me. I quickly calculated two outcomes – I was either going to die because of the newly discovered problem or, eventually, I was going to die of something else. As a devout, yet mildly militant agnostic, I managed to shut down the thought paths that led to outcomes where available information missed huge chunks of certainty. At that first stage, *we* knew virtually nothing other than there was a lump and there needed to be some tests to see how nasty it was.

Ali was the sort of person that needed to compute and then worry about all the possible what ifs. I have always said to her that when it came to a genuine crisis in our family, she was far better prepared to handle it than me because she had lived through it at least once already. Lived through it on an emotional level, in her head. I refused to comprehend any sort of cataclysmic situation (that was usually related to my children) as those truly dark thoughts were far too painful to burn away within the innermost depths of my brain.

Furthermore, although not particularly fashionable to admit, I considered myself a man's man. I never liked to make a fuss about things. I made every effort to be present physically, and financially, and remain emotionally strong for my wife and my family. I knew I couldn't prevent every problem that life had to offer them and despite my urge to protect them from all evils, I also understood that exposure to some parts of life (even when painful) would be necessary. For me to feel like I was fulfilling my role as a husband and father – it had been vital that I was chief protector and when I was in town, everything was going to be all right. I strived to be everyone's dependable rock and I was more than happy to have them cling on tight to that, all perfectly nice and safe.

Not that that news suddenly stopped me feeling like a man – it just meant I needed to fortify my emotions to make sure that my wife (and therefore the boys and Lydia) knew that I could cope just fine and there was no point in worrying about things we didn't know about. That would all be a waste of energy. I was pleased to report that I did get to the place I needed to be. Everyone knew the analogy of seeing the duck on the pond, serenely gliding by, but we never see the duck's feet under the water, paddling like fury.

Well, believe it or not, that wasn't me.

Genuinely.

I clicked into autopilot and, figuratively, my feet paddled. The parts nobody could see were just as calm and serene as the parts they could. No panic, no worries, don't ask me how I did it. I just did it. I had to.

Having said all that, I did cry down the phone.

I was sure I told Ali what the doctor had said to me word for word. Neither of us would remember any other details of that call. There were a lot of expressions of love, a lot of *let's not jump to conclusions,* and different incantations of *staying positive helps.*

Now, when I said I cried – I wasn't a bawling mess of snot and tears (not that there would have been anything wrong with that), but the mixture of feeling sorry for myself and the sense of guilt for thoughts that I'd let the whole family down by getting ill, manifested itself physically. There was a constriction, a pain, that took over my throat, a dignified cracking of my voice, followed by three or four tears that broke loose and escaped down the sides of my face as I lay there on my back. I told Ali that I was glad that I had shared all my shit with her, and I felt much better that she now knew as much as I did. She was right beside me on my darkened path. A problem shared is a problem halved, or so they say.

Maybe it was the best way to cope with the fear. The fear was not as insurmountable because I'd enlisted my favourite person to help me face it.

Straight after that phone call, whilst I felt a touch better, Ali tried to get up from the armchair but, in her new-found distress, discovered her legs had lost their willingness to co-operate. A pins-and-needles-like sensation raged through Ali's legs, but before she dropped back into the chair or, worse, down to the floor, Harrison ran over and grabbed her. Our eldest had witnessed her take the call and held her until at least the sensation of feeling crippled had eased. The relief for Ali was temporary. Shock came back within an hour and with a renewed vengeance, she collapsed down to the hard stone tiles of the kitchen floor. She sprawled out, but she didn't care what her arms and legs did, and she let herself sob uncontrollably as she realised that her safe, loving, dependable world had been blown wide open.

At the time, Ali felt the devastation was absolute. She could not find the presence of the fraction of a molecule of hope that hid, silently, about a million miles away.

Silver Linings

I wouldn't have said that I was a particularly positive person. I used to find those people that were ridiculously positive a bit of an annoyance, so I tried never to act like that. However, it was also true that I'd be disappointed if those that knew me well described me as negative. Generally, I stayed near to a neutral charge with brief flirts into the realms of both positivity and, just as frequently, negativity. A typical Brit.

For some weird reason, I had edged myself toward the positive end of the spectrum. People say that, don't they? *Stay positive.* Positive Mental Attitude. I could be a believer in that philosophy, but the realist in me also held me back from full subscription to that mantra, because I struggled with - if I just *think* positive - then such-and-such will (or won't) happen? I was never convinced that that was how it worked, but one thing was for sure, worrying about shit that may never happen, or crap that I had no control over, was not healthy for my mind. And if it wasn't healthy for my mind, I was sure it would manifest itself somehow and harm my body. Stress has always been a killer – of that, I was certain.

One hurdle to get over was that I couldn't *make* myself be positive. Of course, I could have a word with myself and make every effort to look on the bright side of life – but if I wasn't in the right mood then the spectre of negativity would find a way to infiltrate my most fortified defence. I found the first day of discovery overwhelming. I was confused, and the whole shock and severity of it all meant a positive or negative status became totally irrelevant. I was never one to crave attention, but I knew I would get it in abundance from family, friends, neighbours, and maybe even the odd work colleague. They would all be extra nice to me and all incredibly supportive. It felt bizarre to think about it. I was scared that all that attention might make the entire debacle seem real.

Everything felt crazy. What was going to happen to me?

The first silver lining was that the sickness seemed to have dissipated. I wondered if my body had decided that there was now a different foe it should be concentrating on. Stop honking your guts up – there was more serious shit to focus on.

It was mid-summer and, like all hospitals, it was baking hot inside because air-conditioning was never going to happen. My internal heat that affected my sweat glands had eased off the throttle. The nausea was in remission, and my temperature levelled out and kept me on simmer - like every other bugger in the building. With the relentless loss of liquid, I had become a good candidate for dehydration. Luckily, I was still plumbed into the drips.

Through my fear, some practical thoughts ran through me. How could I *not* feel a lump inside of me? How come, until the sickness bug, I had felt perfectly well? I had lost weight and the last check-up I had gave me positive results. Twenty-four hours previously I considered myself fit and well. What the hell was going on? I reasoned with all of that and concluded, the very positive conclusion, that I couldn't be fitter and better prepared for whatever the battle was going to be. If strength was required, then I was ready for it. Better now than when I'm old and frail.

Inspiration can come from anywhere. When Argentina made the decision back in the 1980s to invade the Falkland Islands, my cousin's husband, Steve, was sent there to carry out his commitment to the Navy, his commitment to our Queen and country. Although we won the war, it hadn't gone particularly smoothly for young Steve. He had been shot in the head. With little hope, he had a shroud pulled over him. Someone read him his last rites. I don't think he heard those rites.

He was expected to die.

Except, he didn't die.

Incredibly, Steve pulled through and made a remarkable recovery. The medical staff did the most miraculous job in bringing him back from the brink. Steve played his part, too. Physio for an injured person could prove to be much harder than a fitness or training session for someone that was physically well. To conquer such a massive test, injured people had to demonstrate unbelievable strength, both mentally and physically. One thing that stuck with me was how Steve was always so grateful to his colleagues in the Navy for the training that got him to peak physical condition. He was convinced that if it wasn't for them, quite simply, he wouldn't have survived.

Steve's story stayed deeply with me, I found it inspirational and although my new situation was with a completely different enemy, I could draw upon Steve's wise words and be optimistic that I was in good enough shape to tackle whatever it was that wanted a war with me.

I felt better that I had dumped half my worries on to my wife. I thought I could halve the problem further by sharing the joy with some others. Armed with my phone, I typed out a message to update my brother and my friends. GaryMan had been my best mate since I was 12 and I knew the reason that he hadn't joined in with the previous day's piss-taking was because he and his wife Sam were in a remote part of North Wales, for a well-deserved long weekend. The pair of them had managed to get away from it all, but that also meant that they had got away from all civilisation, and that included Wi-Fi and even a half-decent phone signal. My news was hardly going to improve GaryMan's holiday experience, so I was happy to leave him out of what had happened to me. He could catch up with everything when he was back. I'd seen the great pictures he'd sent over (he must have been able to locate a solitary bar of signal from somewhere) and it looked like he was having fun and getting smashed like the lovable rogue that he was, and there was no way I wanted to piss on his parade.

Sean and Panda seemed to be having a pleasant weekend as well. Sean was out with his family and Panda was enjoying a biking-come-getting-pissed trip along the Grand Union Canal with a different group of friends. I'd let them all know tomorrow and maybe, by then, I would know some more. With a bit of luck, I would not be answering yes to Sean's question of - Will you have a colostomy bag?

GaryMan's message came through: -

> Garyman: Sorry mate, Sam and I are in
> Snowdonia staying in a treehouse, and no coverage.
> Just seen all these messages are you okay?
> What's happened? Apart from getting wanked
> off by the doctor.

I chose not to spill the beans. At least not yet. Instead, I told him (and therefore the rest of the group) that I still had either suspected appendicitis or constipation. GaryMan came back with 'You pussy' punctuated with the standard laugh emoji.

Richard, my big brother also in the group, already knew my problem was not a stuck poo because we had exchanged some direct messages. Texts were not really the medium for serious stuff, so I decided to give him a call and talk to him properly.

I called Richard and it was a good, positive conversation. He let me retell my story and we discussed the bare facts. I knew Richard was worried but he, like me, reinforced that there was little point in stressing over anything we didn't know or anything we couldn't control. Recently he and his wife Helen, had lived through enough illness themselves, and they, with a dollop of help from the NHS, conquered the serious times admirably. Richard was quick to dismiss any speculation at all, despite his hypochondria. I reckon I had my shit together and did my best to reassure him that I was in pretty good shape, considering what had happened and what I had been told. We spoke of practical matters, and he offered to call up our dad so that I didn't have to. I had hit the point of not wanting to retell my story anymore. I felt bad that my dad might not be happy that he was being updated second-hand, but I was exhausted with everything and needed to save up enough positive energy to be strong enough to reassure my mum that I was all right. Richard said he'd do his best to make sure people weren't going to bother Ali - unless there was good reason to. Richard played the part of big brother perfectly, and I thanked him for it.

Whilst my phone still had battery, and I was equally as charged,

I was in the right mood to make the call to my mum. Soon after I became a parent myself, I understood how much my mother must love and care for her sons. It was a ridiculously powerful feeling. I've already explained how I block out thoughts that breached the world of grief, sadness and devastation, and I instantly shut down any scary thoughts of losing a child. A journey down that path was too frightening for me. It had better not break the magic, but since Ali and I had become parents, every single wish I had been granted (a successful wishbone battle, blown out birthday candles, blown away eyelashes), I have taken and asked whoever was the Wish-Granter, to ensure I died before any of my three children. Maybe I had wished too forcefully over many years, as it would be a bit mean (and hypocritical) of me to pop my clogs as I hit fifty and destroy my Mum's right to leave the planet in the correct order.

There were only a couple of rings before Mum answered. I had sent her a text to let her know I intended to call her and since then she had been sat at home filled to the brim with anxiety as she waited to hear her son's voice. As I dialled the number and waited for that answer, I wondered how the conversation would go. Having spoken to Ali and Richard, I felt stronger, and the plan (from my end) was to only send out positive vibes. My mum could be a sensitive flower, yet when it came to important and serious matters, she had always come through with impressive mental toughness. She was also no mug, so I knew I had to be honest because she would have seen right through any attempt to hide anything. Luckily, I didn't know everything, so I was able to down play the situation without having to lie.

Age was irrelevant. My mum was in her seventies, and I was 50, but I would always be her baby son. She told me so. As a parent myself, I totally got why she had been desperate to hear from me. I'd die for my children, and I inherited that mandate from her. I knew she had done some tough yards at home, all on her own as she'd split from my dad when I was very young. I had updated Ali over the previous 24 hours' activities, and she had passed on most of it to her mother-in-law, but it was never going to be the same as direct contact.

Mum did not let me down. The conversation was remarkably normal, neither of us got upset, there was the undertone of an elephant on the line, but we remained strong for each other. I behaved very much as normal me (or so I thought) and I was honest when I explained how much better I felt.

'You're not just saying that to make me feel better?' she asked.

'No. Honestly. I feel OK now. A bit tired, but definitely on the right path.'

I could sense Mum's relief as we casually discussed how I was emotionally (in a positive frame of mind), and how I was sorry to scare and worry everyone, and to explain that everything must be just fine because I felt a hundred times better than I did. Because we were so chatty, I probably relayed some information that Ali had possibly held back. I mentioned my pancreas and she picked up on it. To quash her concerns before she jumped to the same grim conclusion I had, I quickly countered that the experts still had umpteen tests to go through and there was every reason to be positive, especially as I didn't have symptoms of anything evil. In fact, I had the opposite of symptoms, I was perfectly fine, so there was a decent chance that all we had to overcome was a cyst or something equally innocuous. I just needed the quacks to clarify it soon, so we could all get a good night's sleep. It was a great call, and my mum felt better that she had heard my voice. I felt better that I had stopped her from worrying herself into an early grave.

We ended the call after we tentatively agreed to meet up the following week, when I was back home. We both said, 'I love you' to each other, which meant a lot as it was only saved for moments when either of us needed to hear those precious words. I wondered if my mum also knew that the main problem with pancreatic cancer was that people didn't get any symptoms until it was all too late.

It was a good call that made me feel better about life and I was pleased that I had made my mum feel better, too. I smiled to myself because I almost believed all the positive things I had said.

Speaking to Ali had been the toughest, heart-wrenching part of the situation, and heaven knew what I was going to say to my three children. There were no words for such an occasion, I hadn't checked, but I was certain that Clintons didn't have a suitable card range to apologise to children that their father was staring death in the face. Fortunately, Ali had that angle covered so that I didn't have to personally cross that bridge. She had told me that Lydia only needed to know that I had been ill, felt better, and that I had to stay in hospital so the doctors could continue to prod me about until they knew exactly what my mystery illness had all been about. So, no lies as such, but just some withheld information that would be rated above PG for a 13-year-old. Ali gave the meaty part of the story to the boys. Their response was typical of men handicapped with my cold-hearted genes; they didn't show much emotion and bordered on unexcited.

Harrison's response was, 'Oh, so we don't truly know anything yet?' And both he and Jayden made the conscious choice of adopting a no-worry-attitude (or at least they showed no signs) until they needed to. What was delightful to hear (but not surprising to hear) was that all three of them had given their mum all the love and support she craved to get her through that first wave.

Whilst I couldn't remember much about that first phone call with Ali, I did know that we discussed a visit and what the process was. The hospital was strict on the rules. Covid had changed everything. The deal was that each patient got one visitor, for a maximum of one hour, at a timeslot that was determined by a call to the help desk on a first come / first served basis. The staff were immovable on it, and there would be no exceptions. I had given the number to Ali, but nobody answered the phone. People couldn't just turn up, without a time, otherwise there would be no visit.

Ali had tried again and again without luck and finally sent me a message to see if I could do anything at my end. Without any warning I became desperate. I had no idea where it had gone, but I had totally lost my cool. Nothing else mattered, I had – HAD – to see Ali. I needed to hold her and convince her that firstly, I was better, and I was strong enough for *any* fight and, together, we would be alright. The urge to see her was undeniable. My desperation was magnified by the fact I knew Ali would be equally as frantic to see me.

Fortunately, there was nothing else to do, so I rang and rang and rang until, inevitably, someone answered. When I wanted to be, I could have been persistent in the extreme. The maniac in me stepped aside whilst I tried to calmly explain my situation. It was probably a similar situation as everyone else that ever dialled that number. The nurse made an apology of sorts, but the fact was that they had far more important matters at that time of day such as serving up all the medication for the troops that day. No problem, I just wanted to bank a time – any time. Grateful that someone had finally picked up the call, I would have accepted anything.

4pm until 5pm you say?

The only time you have?

Great. Book it. Done. Sorted.

Blood pressure decreasing to normal levels.

Relax.

The verdict I received earlier that day meant that there was to be no appendectomy. To confirm this, a nurse used a cloth to wipe away the N-B-M written in black marker pen on the whiteboard above my bedhead. It was an action that declared to the world that I was now allowed hospital food. I tried my best to remain positive. I had missed the opportunity to order a regimented dinner, although the nurse that told me that also offered to hunt down a bowl of soup and some bread if I wanted it. Although it had been several hours since I'd stopped being sick, I still didn't feel hungry. Like a wounded soldier in recovery, I needed some nutrition. Some energy, to keep my strength up as my mother would have said. I settled on a cup of white coffee and a digestive biscuit. Silver lining? I had to say aluminium lining, and that was about as positive as anyone could have been when it came to the food in any NHS establishment.

Michael

The news was still fresh, yet I managed to avoid thoughts of death. What that meant was that I didn't analyse my early death. A quick, yet painful, early, tragic death. A death, over the next six-months where I would lose several stones in weight, spend every precious moment either in hospital or in a hospice rigged up to a machine to endure painful chemotherapy, radiology and whatever new drugs they wanted to test on me. No hair, no strength, constant pain, sickness (that got worse and worse) all day and, more cruelly, all fucking night. I would waste away in front of my wife and kids until they held my hand and let me drift off into eternity whilst they whispered that they loved me as I floated off and exhaled for that final time.

That probably wasn't strictly true. I wasn't a cyborg and scary thoughts did sprout and develop and made themselves heard in my head. The fears were too much for me to comprehend so I did my best to only entertain them for a moment before I assigned them to their own quick, premature death. If it was to be curtains for me, I wasn't going to let cancer have the pleasure of stealing everything away from me. No way would I let the fear of it consume me. No way could that fucking tumour, which came from fuck-knows-where, engulf and digest my hope. As I lay in bed number 4, I sensed that my strength had returned and therefore my spirit was, at that point, unbreakable.

One thing that dragged me through my ordeal was a sense of humour. I'd admit to possessing a dark and sometimes sick, sometimes offensive, sense of humour. People may already have been offended by some of the questionable things I've already said, or some things they might hear in the future, and for that, I was (almost) sorry. I'd always been a bit old-fashioned and a bit misogynistic to some people. I would have definitely taken the piss out of anyone; no one was safe. I don't hold back. It wouldn't have mattered who you were, what you looked like, where you were from, what you sounded like, what you wore, what you did, what you said, what sky-fairy you believed in, whose genitals you enjoyed the most...as far I was concerned, nobody was off-limits. It was all about inclusion and I honestly subscribe to that. Fortunately, I did have a half-decent filter. That's what we called being marginally sensitive - having a filter.

If I believed someone was going to get upset about being the butt of a joke of mine, I would at least have the decency to do it behind their back. Never to their face. To have a filter is imperative and mine was maintained (by me) so I didn't get beaten up, jailed or disowned by my friends and family or worse, blocked on social media. I valued the importance of a sense of humour, possibly more than anything else. If I were to lose it, then it would mean my spirit would become vulnerable. No - worse than that. If I couldn't laugh about the ridiculous mess I was in; all the needles, the sheer loss of dignity and all the shit my friends had come out with, then I really think I would have been well and truly on the slippery slope to depression and oblivion. I vowed to keep the jokes alive and to find laughs in the bizarre – until I couldn't find it funny.

I had become mobile by Saturday afternoon. The medics had finally relieved me of the intravenous drip that bound me to the bed. That was because I was no longer puking and was able to take in water in the more conventional, oral way. The cannula remained in place like a permanent mosquito that sat on my arm and I still had to make sure I was rigged up to my bed every few hours to take in the antibiotics, but with the restrictions lifted, my state of mind had improved. I passed by Michael on my way to the bathroom, but the curtains between us were open, so it felt more normal to walk past, eyes fixed dead ahead of me, no effort to offer a greeting, even though I knew Michael lay there. It felt rude of me, but only a little bit. I justified my impoliteness to myself because it was the by-product of the gift of privacy and space to my neighbour. He wouldn't have wanted me around to invade his sight and thoughts every time I walked by.

After I failed to strain out a poo, yet again, I made the return journey and then I did attempt to make eye contact with Michael the neighbour. I beamed a smile (facemasks were off for us patients and my now daily Covid test was still negative) and said, 'You alright?'

It was probably the same conversation we'd had before.

'Yeah,' Michael answered.

I stopped. I don't know why I thought this, but he looked like he wanted to talk. 'How long have you been here?'

'I come in on Fursday.' Maybe his voice was distorted by the tube that went into his throat.

Maybe it was due to twenty years of his abuse of Bensons and Hedges. Judgemental Phil registered his rough voice, terrible pronunciation and an accent that would not be heard on the BBC News desk anytime soon. Common as muck. I know those thoughts made me sound like an insufferable snob, but I was being honest - it was what I thought. If he had been one of my kids, I would have been mildly horrified and I would have corrected them in an instant: 'I *CAME* in on *THURS*day!' But Michael wasn't one of mine, so I was never going to correct him. Behind his brown eyes I saw the fear, confusion and pain. Somehow, we were in the same place together for some reason or other.

Frightened to know the truth, maybe they paired us up because we had the same problem.

I asked, 'What are you in for?'

'Er....my stomach was bad,' Michael explained. He was slightly goofy, and I noticed his front teeth protruded through his stubbly mouth as he spoke. Some people had mouths that I couldn't help but look at when they spoke, rather than having tractor-beam eyes that couldn't be denied.

Michael pointed at his stomach through the light blue sheet that covered him.

I stood at the foot of his bed but couldn't help but notice the dirt in his fingernails.

'I had an operation....to take out some ulcers.'

There were pauses as he spoke so he could swallow. I could tell the tube bothered him. It stopped him from talking naturally.

I patted my throat and asked with genuine concern, 'Is that tube hurting you?'

Michael suddenly shrank back like I had just reminded him that he was in pain. His eyes could not hide his sorrow. Like a wounded mongrel on an RSPCA advert, his eyes told a story of distress and anyone with a heart would want to help that vulnerable soul. He didn't say anything, but he simply responded with three slow nods. For a moment, I thought he might cry. It was strange, since he looked like a tough character. I had already deduced that Michael had most likely had a difficult childhood, possibly on the brink of poverty and with little opportunity and, although he'd battled through all of that hardship, I could see he was upset about his illness and all the hospital shit.

'Have you had any painkillers? They should be able to sort you out,' I suggested.

Michael nodded some more. 'Yeah. They give me sumfink...dunno what it was.'

A nurse sped up to us and announced to Michael that she had come to give him a wash. He looked like he needed it badly. His brown hair appeared matted and greasy and he still had the same dirty look about him from when I first clapped eyes on him. He hadn't moved from that bed since before I had arrived, he hadn't needed to go the bathroom because he was firmly rigged up with the catheter, but he also hadn't been able to freshen up in the bathroom. I wondered how much time had passed since he'd even brushed his teeth. I wondered if he owned a toothbrush let alone brought it with him. I imagined that he probably stank of BO and I kept my distance whilst at the same time I was fascinated to find out exactly how awful his BO might have been. I still had the slick of sweat on me from the combination of the infection and the heat of the summer, but at least I had deodorant to give my armpits a fighting chance. Michael, well he didn't look like the sort of guy that believed in such luxuries.

'Well, I will leave you to it,' I said as I moved over to my end-of-terrace.

The nurse set down a bowl of warm soapy water and swished the curtains dramatically after me. She didn't say too much whilst she gave the man a bed bath. The things the nurses had to do. They were possibly de-sensitised to those sorts of tasks; having to clean up my puke and washing the bollocks of a spectacularly dirty man. How was your day, darling? Fucking marvellous.

The sploshes continued behind the screen. I finished my book about Walter Payton and read about his death. When I took in those last few chapters, I reflected on the story and, to be honest, I didn't like the book quite half as much as I wanted to. Most of the parts about his sporting achievements were good enough and plenty of it was memorable, but something missed for me. People say, never meet your heroes. I guess I loved to watch him run with the ball so much that I should have just resigned to be sat in front of the television set where I could binge watch Walter's highlight reels. Although, it could have been that my mind was elsewhere, and maybe I hadn't let the words in the book transport me away to a faraway place. Instead, I had been detained in Bay 4.

I put the book in my bedside unit and felt a pang of guilt. I considered what I thought about Michael. Dirty, poor, common, and no doubt as thick as pig-shit. Jesus, what a horrible, prejudiced bastard I'd become. What a disgusting trait to have. I recognised that awful characteristic in myself and, I guessed, at least it was a positive step to help me overcome my ugly bigotry.

Like many middle-aged, middle-classed, straight, white males, I'd had a pretty smooth ride in the game of life compared to other groups. I appreciated how exceptionally lucky and very privileged my life had been. I didn't feel good about blanking Michael and to not even give him a chance toyed with my conscience. On the other hand, there was every possibility that the man wouldn't have given a shit if I considered his feelings or not.

I decided to tackle my prejudiced behaviour head on. I made a moral decision to keep the ugly side of me in check. I understood where it was rooted, where it came from and how it manifested itself within me. As I thought about the situation, I realised how my own intolerant attitude actually altered my behaviour. In my defence, I reasoned that it could well be an animal instinct, like an in-built condition, where I felt threatened by things (people) that were 'different' and therefore, doused in ignorance, I would arm myself with a metaphorical pitchfork.

My prejudices did not mean I was a racist. Someone once told me that there were many other reasons to dislike someone than simply the colour of their skin and I found that was very true for me. The truth was, I generally didn't like people. Those close to me knew that I found our species a horrible, destructive, aggressive animal that seemed to be hell-bent on a mission to destroy planet Earth and therefore itself. I often referred to our species (to all of us) as 'The Human Plague'.

The member of the plague called Michael was in a right mess and so was I. I had a choice - be friendly with the guy or be quiet and keep to myself and my own thoughts.

The bottom line was that I felt sorry for him. I had spoken to Ali and my brother a few times on the phone but kept my voice down because Michael didn't even possess a phone. *Who doesn't have a phone these days?* Neither of us had seen any visitors but at least I had some comfort in the knowledge that Ali would be with me soon enough. I had a strong suspicion that Michael had nobody. I felt sad that he was on his own.

I hated the idea that anyone that was sick, was equally alone. So, I just couldn't avoid Michael. I couldn't be that rude and just distance myself and deliberately ignore the man that suffered without any support. I searched within myself to find some understanding and some compassion. I didn't plan on writing out an application form to foster the man, but I could at least be pleasant and civil.

A new nurse took some more blood from me. More tests apparently. Whatever.

I was already at the stage where I didn't care what they did to me. Both arms were bruised around the crook of each elbow and the cotton wool balls came and later went after each visit. The tape they had used to hold things on to my skin were of an industrial strength. I sent a picture of my purple and red inner arms to my mates. I tagged it with: *My audition for* Trainspotting 3 *is going well.*

Physically, I was on the right path and genuinely felt much better. The medicine must have been good stuff. However, I had become terribly bored of the hospital, or bored of being held captive. I wanted to recuperate from the madness in the comfort of my own home. It was the simple things that got to me. Yes, it was true that I wanted to see Ali and the kids (every moment was going to be significantly precious), but I craved a decent cup of tea and the use of my own toilet. I told myself that if I dwelled on those thoughts there would be no point, a complete waste of mental energy. I knew I had to stay for more blood tests, intravenous medicine and the nurses were there to monitor my obs every few hours. They gave me some socks, which I accepted gladly. After I asked what they were for, the nurse told me that I needed to wear them to help prevent blood clots. God, what with the injections as well, they seemed obsessed with blood clots. I didn't quite see the exact point of it, as I hadn't had surgery and wasn't expected to meet up with any scalpels anytime soon. Despite my challenge, I relented, and put them on with no further fuss. After all, to pull on a pair of *brand new* socks was one of *the* best things in the whole wide world.

Fantastic.

Nope. Not Fantastic.

My ecstasy was short-lived. The free socks were a con. They weren't complete. I had pulled on the first shiny navy stocking (I never knew the exact mix of fabric, but they were silkier than cotton) on to my right foot and - PING!

My toes popped right out of the end.

Rather than there being extra reinforcement where the ball of my foot would be – there was a ruddy great hole! The untold pleasure to slip on some lovely new socks had been stolen from me.

Today, of all days.

I inspected the damaged goods only to find that they weren't officially damaged. The hole was more of an opening and the edges were intentionally sewn so I concluded that the socks had been designed and made deliberately to have a hole where the ball of the foot should be. *What kind of sick bastard invented those?* I snatched the other one out of the cellophane wrapper and, as feared, that one had exactly the same hole, too. Bollocks.

Disappointed and disgusted at the tarnished freebie, I angrily yanked the socks on and had to fiddle about with the ends, so my toes didn't escape out of that ridiculous opening.

Aha! It suddenly came to me.

Michael hadn't worn the worst, holiest socks known to man after all! He had worn new socks, a fresh pair identical to mine. Bless him, and there was me, with thoughts that he might have been a tramp. I had thought that. Silly me. Silly, *judgemental* me.

A short while before Ali's 4pm slot, two female physios arrived at Michael's bed. They wanted him up.

'Come on Michael,' they ordered, a bit too chirpily. 'Swing your legs around over here and let's see if you can stand up.'

Michael didn't give anything verbal back to the small team. There was no objection and there was no agreement either. Suffice to say that actions spoke louder than words and he did play ball with them. Slowly, whilst they coaxed him, Michael shuffled about and managed to dangle his skinny legs over the side of the bed that faced me. The physio duo stationed themselves either side of their patient. Up until then his body had been half-covered with a bedsheet so the physique of the man had not been apparent. As he sat, getting ready to stand for the medical team, he seemed weak and gaunt, like a new-born fawn that was to take its first tentative steps. I felt compelled to join in, although I was sure the two experts did not need any of my unqualified help. The main physio wanted Michael to take a few steps and go for a short walk. As much as I was sure they knew their job, I couldn't help but think that he barely had the strength to move a leg to the side of the bed, let alone pace around the ward. I had flashbacks to Roald Dahl's story of Grandpa Joe Bucket, stuck in bed for 50 years (with three other oldies and associated disability benefits) and then, suddenly, a free trip to a chocolate factory was on the cards and he was up like a flash – with all the songs, dances and more skipping than a boxer's training camp. I always wondered if Grandpa Joe lost his benefits after the appropriate investigation.

Michael's motivation wasn't a lifetime supply of chocolate, but the gift of being able to go home.

'Go on, mate,' I called. I was not sure why I had referred to him as *mate,* but I had my theory. A theory centred around my reptilian brain. My reptile of choice seemed to be the chameleon. I had developed an (annoying) urge to alter my demeanour to suit the people that I communicated with. When I saw myself change, I would hate myself for it. If I spoke to a car mechanic or a builder at work – dare I say, working class people – it wouldn't take long before I would say, 'Alright mate' and swear ten times more than I normally would. And, as the perfect chameleon, another change would happen whenever I spoke with people far more classy or intelligent than me and I'd equally hate the posher, pretentious Phil. I strived (and failed) to be more like Harrison. That guy had always been consistent, more gecko than chameleon, and never needed to change anything about his demeanour as a defence mechanism. Unlike me.

I carried on with the encouragement of my *mate.*

'Just see if you can stand up first and if it doesn't work out, they'll catch you. Just stand there for a minute and see how it goes.' Who the hell did I think I was? Who was I to involve myself in that bloke's rehabilitation?

Michael only let out a few grunts as he complied with all our encouragement. I couldn't make out if he made the noises as a reaction to pain or just because it was hard work. The metal side bars that had safely kept him on the bed had been clanged downwards to allow his exit. Slowly, both of Michael's feet (with socks) touched the floor for the first time in days. The physios held him under his armpits and supported him whilst he let his backside slide off the mattress. He naturally transferred all his scrawny frame through his legs and even though he looked weak and unsteady, he did it. There was a noticeable stoop, but he managed to stand.

'Yes, mate!' I called out loud. 'See how that feels. Just stand there for a while and get your balance sorted.'

He must have summoned up some hidden strength from deep within because he handled the momentous event superbly. I was impressed and I decided to take a step back from my cheerleader activities and let the experts take it away. Silently, I continued to observe the scene.

All three of them, Michael and his two physios, did a fantastic job. After he managed to stand for a couple of minutes, they coaxed Michael to take some tentative steps. Several bags of various liquids were attached to the man, including a large bag of orange urine that had slowly collected waste. I saw that the physio team were used to that added task. The other bags seemed to contain darker fluids such as stomach juices and blood. I watched on, eager to know if Michael had the strength to fulfil the demands of the physio team. One of them grasped the back of Michael's gown to make sure his bony arse didn't expose itself to us spectators as he began his walk. They told him that from now on, he should continue to make every effort to get out of bed and walk about. It would all help massively towards his recovery and enable him to get home much sooner. That is, on the assumption that he had a home.

Michael did remarkably well. They took him out for a good five minutes and I imagined that they must have walked him out of Bay 4 and then into the corridor, then a shuffle around, and then back to the safety and comfort of his bed. They helped him get back into bed and busied around to reset his side bars, plump the pillows and they made sure the sheets were all nice and neat. Michael complied with everything whilst they fussed over him without saying a word. The lead physio looked delighted with Michael's excursion to the corridor and back and said that she now expected him to able to move about as much as he liked. As long as he could carry his bags with him.

They both left him and cheerily proclaimed, 'See you tomorrow.'

'Well done, mate.' I couldn't hide my pride in his efforts. 'How was that? Are you OK?'

'Yeah. It was alright. They said I need to keep movin' abaaht and ven I can go 'ome.'

'Where is home? Do you live near here?' I asked, tentatively and tactfully, as judgemental me was half-expecting the answer to be a tent or a cardboard box.

'Langley,' Michael confirmed.

Obviously not the Langley in the USA, the home of the FBI that every Jason Bourne film referred, but the Langley next to Slough. My snobby brain computed that Langley was a credible answer. Slough was indeed a strange enough place. Nobody would say they've lived in Slough. It was a big enough town for people to say they lived in Cippenham or Burnham Borders, Chalvey, Wexham, Britwell or somewhere else, but never just Slough. Each area seemed worse than the next. If I was miles away from home, maybe in a different country and someone asked me where I lived, I might have said London or maybe West London, if I thought they only had a little knowledge about UK geography. Other times I may have said that I lived ten minutes from Windsor - if I believed they did have some appreciation of our geography, the Queen or Legoland. Windsor always looked so attractive on television whenever they broadcast something or other about the Royals. One thing I would have never said was - five minutes from Slough Central. If ever a place needed a re-brand, it was Slough.

Langley could be a bit hit and miss. There were some lovely houses nestled within some quiet, friendly roads. It boasted a convenient location near to Heathrow and the M4 and M25, there were some decent state-run grammar schools within the borough, and it wasn't that cheap to live there. Unfortunately, the sad truth was that a lot of Langley was shit, and I did think of it as Slough's younger brother, trying to escape from being tarred with the same shitty brush. Who was I trying to kid? I had a Slough postcode.

'We got a flat in Langley,' Michael completed his answer.

'We?' I carried on the conversation. 'Do you live with your family?'

'Yeah, me missus just had a baby two mumfs ago.'

'Two months ago? Seriously?' I couldn't help but smile, and thoughts of Langley instantly took a back seat. 'Wow! Congratulations!' I felt genuinely pleased for him, and he responded with a reciprocated daft grin and I witnessed his brown eyes come alive. I sensed it was probably his most favourite topic of conversation just by how animated his grubby face had become.

'Fanks,' he said, his voice soppy.

'And here you are in hospital! You need to get yourself well and get back to helping your missus. Is this your first?'

'Nah,' Michael carried on with his slow nods (even though he should have shaken his head for a negative answer). His soppy grin looked like it might be in place for a long time.

'How many do you have?'

'Two. 'Ve oldest one just turned one and now we got the baby.'

'Bloody hell!' I exclaimed, 'You've been busy in lockdown! It's never easy looking after a baby in that first year and you've got two! How is your missus doing? Is she OK coping with all of that baby stuff whilst you're lording it up in here?'

'Yeah. She's alright,' Michael responded positively.

I detected the tiniest lull in his enthusiasm, so maybe she wasn't completely alright. There was no way I was going to challenge him on my suspicion. The true situation of Michael's partner's wellbeing hung in the air between us.

Michael broke the pause. 'I don't know your name.' He was almost proud of the fact that he didn't know my name.

'I'm Philip,' I answered whilst I patted my chest which I hope didn't appear patronising, like I was talking down to someone that didn't know any English. 'And you're Michael, right?'

'Yeah,' he answered.

I wondered if he thought, *How does this knobhead know my name?*

In my entire adult life, I don't think I had ever introduced myself as Philip. I had no idea why I suddenly decided to change from 'Phil' for the benefit of our new relationship. I could only assume that because all the medical staff had referred to me as Philip (and the fact that it was my name) then it made some sense to keep everything consistent. Whilst I resided in that hellhole, I figured I might as well be Philip and then when I got out – I could make a return as me, return to being Phil.

Every time Michael called me Philip, it absolutely tickled me. He'd say it a lot whenever we spoke and I don't know why but it seemed that he would make a concerted effort to pronounce my name properly, like it was the poshest word he'd ever said. It never sounded like it was piss-take. Whenever I thought about how he said my name, it put a silly smile on my face.

'Have you got children, Philip?' Michael asked me back, really getting into the art of conversation.

'Yes, I have. I've got two grown up boys and my daughter is thirteen. And you? What are your two?'

'Yeah, my two are bowf girls.' Michael's eyes were still burned brightly and the nods continued.

'That's great. My daughter is such an energy in the house. Sometimes a little demanding, but she's great fun.'

'Yeah,' said Michael, coupled with his friendly, inane grin.

'You know, we both need to get ourselves well and get the hell out of this place and back to our family,' I said, and allowed Michael to join in with my masterplan.

'Yeah,' came Michael's favourite reply, and then he added, 'I'm definitely givin' up ve fags. I told ve doctor. They're no good for me. I aint smokin' no more, Philip. Because I need to get bet'er.'

'That's superb, mate. Good for you.' I was happy to keep Michael's epiphany buoyant even though I mentally gave him odds of 100/1 to crack the habit. The odds were long simply because I didn't think he had the skills to beat smoking on his own, so I asked, 'Does your missus smoke?'

'Yeah, she does,' Michael answered. I saw that his spark dimmed like before, and maybe he was ashamed that their favourite hobby was smoking cigarettes. 'But...' it was childlike, the way he dug out his enthusiasm again,' she says she'll stop wiv me.'

'OK. Well, that is tough, if one of you still smokes that makes it harder. Look, I'm no expert but I reckon giving up smoking without help is really difficult. If you are serious about quitting you should speak to one of the doctors here, I'm sure they would jump at the chance to offer you some guidance.'

'Yeah. You're right, Philip.' Michael's standard response of *yeah* had become more serious. 'I got COPD, so I gotta stop.'

I didn't know what COPD was, so I asked, 'COPD? What's that?'

'Oh.' He looked surprised, like he thought everyone knew what COPD was. 'It's a lung fing. It just means I have trouble breavin' properly.'

'Really? Then you really must stop smoking. You need to be there for your family, Michael.' I said the words, but was not convinced they'd spark Michael into action.

Michael's response was serious. 'I stopped last year 'cos I was bad wiv it and I was in here, in hospital like. It was when all vat Covid stuff was startin'. It was horrible, Philip. Nobody knew what was goin' on. Everyone was masked up and they said that I was safe from catchin' it – you know, because I wasn't on the Covid ward. But I saw 'em, I saw 'em wheelin' out people in black bags. People was dyin', Philip. I got scared cos vey told me if I got it, wiv me breavin' and everyfin' that I could get it bad. I got so scared, I just got up an' left. I went home.'

I could tell that Michael had been truly frightened whilst the worst of the Covid crisis raged on. I knew that those people that didn't have a healthy respiratory system were more vulnerable than the rest. Those first few months in our hospitals must have been complete carnage. What the staff saw and what they had to endure during the spring of 2020, I can only imagine. The doctors and nurses that looked after me wore facemasks, but they weren't fully PPE'd up with plastic visors, disposable bio-hazard suits, blue overshoes and gloves, and although I could picture it, it must have been terrifying for all the patients *and* all the medical staff. A year and a half later and the world had learnt so much. The panic (and number of fatalities) had certainly levelled out, but the cases and variants spiked and changed continually despite the vaccination programme. The daily tests at Wexham gave me some comfort that they monitored the situation as best as they could, but I had no idea as to how they would respond if there was a sudden outbreak at the hospital.

'I don't blame you for escaping,' I agreed. 'It must have been frightening.'

'Yeah. It was.' Michael's demeanour stayed low. 'Boaf my mum and dad died last year. Wivin a year of each uvver.'

'Seriously? Ah, I'm sorry to hear that, Michael. I don't know what to say.' What does anyone say when the person they're talking to drops that bombshell into the conversation? 'Was it Covid-related?'

'Nah, COPD. They boaf died here. The funeral for my dad was massive, Philip. Mum's as well.' Michael perked up again. Even though it was a subject so raw and personal, he got particularly excited as he told me about his parent's funerals. 'Everyone was there, so many people. Cars, horses, flowers, evreefin'! Best funeral ever, Philip. Ya know vey'd boaf been ill for ages, so it's a good fing that they're at peace now, innit?'

'Yeah,' I confirmed in my most comforting voice. 'As sad as it is, at least you can all take comfort knowing that their suffering is over.' I tried to keep the air of positivity alive.

Unfortunately, Michael's eyes told me that he still suffered from the emotional grief – the pain had still been present.

'I really miss 'em, Philip,' said Michael, and his misery and sadness sounded tangible.

Shit, one of us was going to cry in a minute. I hoped to God that it wasn't me.

I needed to change the subject as tactfully as I could because Michael's stare felt intense. I guessed that, although he looked directly at me, his thoughts were miles away as he remembered good times with his much-loved parents. I could sense how upset he was as he realised that those times were over.

'Do you have any brothers or sisters?' I asked, with the hope that the man hadn't become an orphan and was fortunate enough to have some close support.

'Yeah,' Michael said for the hundredth time. I was grateful that I had broken his stare. It seemed that he had shifted from the darkest place of his thoughts to a marginally better place, somewhere with a little more light. 'I got free bruvvers and two sisters.'

'Must have been tough for you all.'

'Mum was amazin', Philip. She looked after all of us.'

Michael's slow nods had returned. I took it as a good sign. 'I bet. Did your mum and dad get to meet your daughter?' I hoped that they had.

'My oldest one, yeah, but not ve baby.'

'That's good, you know, that they got to know *one* of your girls.'

'Yeah. My mum loved kids, Philip.' Michael had looked away towards the big window in front of us, and then down at his hands that rested in his lap.

There was a pause between us. It wasn't an awkward pause, but it was more of a natural break to absorb all the words that we'd shared between us. We'd discussed family, illness, Covid and the death of Michael's parents. Pretty intimate issues to discuss. I wondered if Michael was going to take my advice to seek out some professional help so he could quit the old coffin nails.

I broke the silence. 'Is your missus coming to see you or is she looking after the baby?'

Michael turned to me again. 'I dunno. If she can sort out a taxi she might come up 'ere.'

'Oh, I take it she doesn't drive.'

'Nah. I don't drive neiver. Well, I can drive but I just never passed the test.' Michael's grin was back and laced with mischief. The smile gave me the impression that maybe he had put himself behind the wheel of a car illegally, many times, and he thought it was cute.

'Oh, OK. Well, hopefully she can get someone to look after the baby and come and see you.'

'Yeah. If she can sort out a taxi,' he repeated.

'Yeah,' I said, complete with inane nods and a dopey grin. I'd become a total dickhead of a chameleon.

Visiting Time

I couldn't put my finger on it, but somehow, I seemed to click with Michael. He was simple in every sense, but there was a childlike honesty about him that I warmed to. Our paths had crossed in a bizarre way and we had found ourselves laid up next to each other in a Slough hospital. Ordinarily, I wouldn't have spent more than two minutes with the guy but, after a few brief conversations, I discovered that we had some fundamental common ground. In a nutshell, there had been undying love for our families and our desperation to get out of 'Hotel Paradise' (as we then called it), and those base things were all that was needed to bond us together. In every other way we were poles apart. We began to use each other to get through each stressful hour, in our mutually parasitic relationship and somehow (we hoped) it would help us get home. That was my plan anyway.

I checked my watch – finally, 4pm approached.

For someone that had suddenly become fearful of not having much time left, the wait until I could physically see Ali had seemed to last forever. Time had been my enemy and it was a crafty, evil enemy at that because I had worked out that the hour slot I had been allowed with Ali would be the fastest hour of the day.

But at last, the wait was over, and Ali had made it. Bang on time.

I heard her voice first. Someone, a nurse I presumed, had taken her temperature with the laser gun and after the beep she must have passed the test because I heard the nurse tell Ali to turn left and she would find me in Bed 4, at the end of the Bay.

'Oh, thank you,' Ali said, from a distance.

My mood and my spirits were already lifted - just in the knowledge that my wife was only yards away. I had turned to face where I knew she would appear at any second.

There was a moment's pause and then, there she was. They had made her wear a face mask so I couldn't see that fantastic smile, but it was definitely there. Five feet nothing of pure loveliness. Beautiful blue eyes (that might have been slightly puffier and wetter than normal due to several bouts of tears), fixed on mine when she turned the corner and headed towards me. I leapt off my bed, and Ali increased her stride and practically bounced into my arms. The hug was a powerful one and I didn't want to let go from it. I wanted to stay in that embrace, safe from the rest of the world and all its suffering, forever.

'Hello Mr,' Ali said gently, as she pulled away from my bear hug. 'How are you doing?'

'A hundred times better now that you're here,' I responded with enthusiasm. 'How are you?'

'Same,' Ali whispered, 'I needed to see you so badly.'

'Tell me about it.' I grabbed Ali back into my arms, to resume our hug. 'I've never needed to see you so much in my life.'

'Oh Phil, what the hell are you doing to me?'

I apologised. 'I'm sorry.' I reclaimed my place on the bed and Ali took the standard issue NHS armchair next to it after she put the bag she had brought with her onto the tray/trolley thing. The bag was baby pink, made of some rubbery latex with *I LEFT MY HEART IN CALIFORNIA* emblazoned in white on the side. I thought - *shouldn't that be San Francisco?* Apparently not.

'Couldn't you have got me a gayer bag?' I joked, sarcastic.

Ali laughed. 'I didn't even think. I've stopped thinking about anything since that call. I just grabbed the nearest bag and threw some things in it. Sorry!'

'It's OK. You know that I'm in touch with my feminine side. I'm just super-glad to see you.'

I told Ali that unless she walked around the hospital, she could take off her mask. She looked around and could see that, apart from the maskless Michael and I, there wasn't anyone else around to infect or be infected. The beds at the other end of the Bay were occupied but they were well beyond the realms of social distancing. Ali took her mask off and gave me one of her precious, loving smiles which included her trademark dimples. Whilst her mouth showed happiness, Ali's eyes betrayed the façade and broadcast her true sentiments without her having to say a single word. I could tell she was scared and desperately worried about me. Much more worried than I was.

'How much do the kids know?' My question was full of dread, but I had to know. I couldn't shift the guilt that I was letting them down. Big, strong, impressive Dad...was not all he was cracked up to be.

'Lydia just knows that you're feeling better, and they're keeping you in here for more tests before you're allowed home. The boys know a bit more about what the scans had revealed and what the tests are looking for. I've spoken to our mums and they're all incredibly worried about you and everyone sends their love.' Ali was straight with me and as usual, she'd pitched spreading the news just right. There was no need to frighten our 13-year-old. We could let her swim about in ignorant bliss until the bubble had to burst.

'It's probably best to not scare anyone until we have a better idea about what we're dealing with.'

'Phil,' Ali became serious. 'Is there anything you haven't told me? Did they actually say the C-word?'

'No. Not directly. Look, I've told you everything I can remember,' I answered truthfully. 'They haven't said the C-word, no. Or at least I don't think they did.' I shouldn't have said that last sentence as I could see it did not impress Ali. My words were supposed to reassure, but they failed me as badly as my pancreas had. 'I really don't think they said it but, sorry, they also didn't say it wasn't either.' I tried my best to not get too deep into the true horror of what we could be faced with. 'Ali, that is what all these tests are about. I'm still staying optimistic that there is every chance we're dealing with a cyst or something benign. I mean, apart from this sickness bug thing, I haven't been ill, and I feel perfectly fine now. Really, I do.'

'Really?' Ali probed.

'Promise.' I settled the matter with my words and my eyes.

I may have salvaged the situation. Ali's eyes didn't leak out salty tears, but that might have only been the case because they'd run dry from earlier sessions. That *date* between us was the most serious one we had ever had on the topic of our health and it looked like neither of us wanted to break down and get upset – that would have easily set the other one off. We had both taken on the role as a rock for each other.

I smiled, to prove that I felt better. Ali had seen more of my smiles than anyone else, certainly more than I had seen, and she could probably tell that I genuinely felt physically well, but she could equally detect the fear and the doubt that lay behind that unique smile. I wondered if she could also sense the guilt I shrouded myself with. Not my most joyous of smiles, but at least I tried.

'Have you seen the Macmillan nurse yet?' Ali asked.

Macmillan had become a chilling word. 'Not yet, no.'

'Can you please ask them why they are involved. You know, Macmillan. Because I'm reading between the lines, and I need to know what we are dealing with here.' Ali said the words that we both thought. She was a few steps ahead of me, as usual. Ali the Brave - prepared to tackle any shit on her terms.

To me, and to many, the name Macmillan represented end-of-life care to patients with terminal cancer. It was a charity that I'd personally supported more than any other. They did the most incredible work under the most dreadful of situations, but I really wasn't ready to see their work up close and personal. Not just yet. Denial was vital to help me through that awful time.

'I will, yes, but until they do all their tests and work out what this is all about, we can't make any conclusions.' Good ol' denial.

'OK.' Ali mirrored my unshakable attitude.

On the inside, we were both shitting ourselves.

'How did you get on with the police?' I had become a master of changing the subject.

'It was alright. Jay made a statement and they said he may need to be a witness if the incident goes to court. He said he would. He was pretty calm about it all.'

'So, everyone is OK?'

'Yes. And *everyone* sends their love.'

The hour, as I knew it would, flew by. We chatted normally and it confirmed that we were both safe and not in any immediate distress. We needed that meet up if only to purge the fear we both experienced since we'd last seen each other. It was a relief to have that time-out to be normal with each other.

'It's been so good to see you,' Ali said as our timeslot came to an end. 'At least you look well.'

'I *AM* well,' I reiterated. It was true, it was the best I'd felt since Thursday afternoon, before that kebab.

'Lydia really wants to see you. The boys do, too. Everyone just wants you home.'

'Well, these sodding Covid rules are a right pain, but we could cheat the system.'

Ali became curious. 'How do you mean?'

'Well, we'll book a time, just like we're supposed to but rather than sit here with me again, we are allowed to go for a walk and get some fresh air and all that. It should be fine because we are allowed to move about and go outside, go for a smoke or make a phone call. They can't really stop us, can they? So how about tomorrow, we'll go for a walk that may just be, accidentally on purpose, to the car park where the gang have been waiting in the car all the time. It doesn't have to be for long, but five minutes would be incredible.'

'That sounds like a plan, Mr Honey.' Ali's eyes sparkled with approval and excitement. The idea was a true winner.

'I know you're the Covid-Queen, so maybe get everyone to do a test before you come but I would love to see them. Prove that I'm doing OK.' Once the plan started to take shape and became real, I latched on to it. It quickly evolved into a target, a goal. That small, achievable milestone was something that I could focus on, and something so significant and precious would help keep my sanity. It was a brilliant plan. Who didn't love a bit of anarchy? Fuck the rules.

Question - Did it qualify as anarchy if everyone involved had taken a lateral flow test?

'OK. I know they're desperate to see you.' Ali was on the same page as me and liked the plan just as much. If the roles had been reversed, Ali would be relentless in a quest to reunite herself with her family.

'Great! That's settled then. It's Sunday tomorrow so I'll let you sort out a time around your roast dinner.'

'Don't worry about that. Do you need me to smuggle some in?' Ali wasn't joking; she knew how much I loved food, especially a Sunday roast.

I laughed. 'No, it's OK.' I pointed to the menu on the tray. 'I'm going to try the roast chicken on the Michelin Star menu we have here. When in Rome...'

'Well, the offer is there.' Ali knew I was making the best of a bad situation. She gave the menu a brief glance, but she wasn't impressed.

Time was up. The beautiful highlight of an awful day was over in a matter of moments. We exchanged 'I Love Yous', our hug was strong and long but, sensibly, we didn't kiss on the lips. I love a bit of anarchy, but neither of us were sure about what infections were still present in or on my body.

I watched Ali leave. I was on a high; it was the best thing about that woeful day. I had restored my hope, my optimism had been reset, and I had a new goal. All of those factors worked as a combination that would drag me through the next 24 hours to when I could hold my children and feel the deep-rooted love of the whole family. I felt stronger, more positive.

I could do this.

At the End of the Day

The business card that she handed to me announced her first name as Christine, however, she introduced herself as Chrissy which sounded friendlier. She was lovely and calm, and I guessed she was about five years younger than me. Like all the staff, she wore a face mask so I couldn't make out all her features, however, she had kind, brown eyes and her shoulder length hair was light brown with reddish highlights in it. As part of her introduction, she told me that she headed up a small team of specialist nurses that were there to act as my conduit to address any questions that I had with the consultants that would look after me. Anything at all, no matter how silly or embarrassing. I was flooded with so many questions that they all jammed together and therefore they stayed back until I sorted an order of priority. Ali and I both wanted clarification as to why Macmillan had been involved quite so immediately, but I was terrified to ask. All I knew was that Macmillan nurses only turned up at the death – ergh, that was a pun that was not intended.

I appreciated that they did the most fantastic, amazing work but that didn't mean I wanted them knocking at my door saying – *Hi, Phil – I'm here for you.* At least, not yet, not without any real warning. Chrissy was a friendlier version of The Grim Reaper than the one I had seen in books and films. For starters, she was armed with business cards rather than a huge scythe. I stared down at Chrissy's card with 'Macmillan Cancer Support' written in their familiar green font, underneath her name and job title. I struggled to comprehend that my life had reached that juncture. Shock and denial were doing a fantastic job with my mindset.

After we exchanged some small talk (Chrissy asked me how I was), I went for it. I had reached the point where I had to know what was going on, whilst at the same time, I pictured Jack Nicolson shouting, *'You can't handle the truth!'*

I held her card in my hand and looked up from the Macmillan logo.

Here goes, I thought.

'Chrissy, I guess my first question has to be, why Macmillan? Does this mean what I think it means?'

'Oh.' Chrissy's tone remained calm and friendly. 'Well, our team is sponsored by the charity, so we have them on our cards and the information that we send out, but we really don't have enough information...'

'So, it's not Game Over just yet then?' I interrupted her because I wasn't convinced that the *sponsorship* thing wasn't simply a ruse to throw me off the scent.

'Oh crikey, NO!' Chrissy seemed horrified that I had jumped to such a scary conclusion.

It seemed a perfectly logical conclusion to me.

'There are a lot of factors in your favour, so you have every reason to believe everything will be fine. You're very young for this sort of thing, your tumour is situated at the tail-end so it should be easier to deal with and it's positive news that this has been caught now. You seem fit and well and that means a lot. They won't be able to confirm exactly what we're up against until they finish all their tests and I would expect that they would need a biopsy at some point. It's important to stay positive.'

I let her words sink in. I could do positive. Sometimes I was a grumpy bastard, especially when I was hungry, but overall, I considered myself a positive soul. I was the luckiest person I knew for starters.

'OK, thanks. I can be positive,' I confirmed back to Chrissy. 'Although, I don't think that I'm particularly young.'

'Believe me, you are.'

'OK, I'm not going to argue with you.' I smiled to show I'd been won over. 'I believe you.' I was making Chrissy's job an easy one. I was confident that my good friends, Mr Shock and Mr Denial, would see me all the way through the storm.

'Good!' Chrissy declared the issue closed. 'Was there anything else that you wanted to ask me?'

I'd heard everything I needed to report back to Ali. There was no way I was going to open any cans of worms and spoil our first meeting.

'Only something practical. I'm covered with private healthcare through work. I was going to call them on Monday, but I don't know how all that works. Fortunately, I've never had to call them before. Is that something you would get involved with?' I planned the question and hoped that conditions for me would improve.

'Possibly. However, in our experience, they probably won't treat you any better than what the specialists here or at Hammersmith are going to do for you. Seriously, they are the best and they will pool all their resources and knowledge from so many different disciplines - because your case involves a few departments. The NHS is very good at the big stuff. We're going to look after you better than anyone. Going private might not necessarily be your best option.'

'Thanks,' I said, as I digested Chrissy's advice. 'Everyone has been brilliant. I think I just had dreams of my own room.'

Chrissy finished off our chat with a truly positive statement. 'Hopefully you will be home before you even have to consider calling them.' And on that note, we said our goodbyes.

Private Healthcare. When else would be a better time to play that particular card that I had up my sleeve? I could have been fast-tracked to a private room with all the comfort and frills that would bring. I had no idea how long I was going to be inside HMP Wexham and the thought of my own ensuite – with proper meals – with my own telly. It did seem incredibly attractive. Before I fully set my heart on the idea I thought - *let's see how this pans out*. As Chrissy had hinted, I might be on the way home before I even needed to bother BUPA.

After Chrissy left me and opened the curtains which exposed me to the world and vice versa. I noticed Michael had become mobile again.

He clearly liked that he could get up, unassisted now, and move about the bay. His bags of various coloured juices were hidden within an Iceland carrier bag, which he held by his side. His very own bag for life.

We had become mates and well beyond the formalities of just a polite nod and an 'Alright?' whenever we saw each other. As Micky Flanagan had already noted, nobody was allowed to acknowledge the same person, in that way, more than twice in the same 24-hour period. Michael had been away from his bed for a while, maybe twenty minutes, and when he returned, he had a sheepish look about him.

'Have you been outside?' I asked.

'Hmm. Yeah.' Michael grinned that grin of his.

'Did you go out for a fag?' I couldn't help but quiz him light-heartedly.

'I did, yeah.' Michael maintained that smile like it was permanently in place. Maybe the wind had changed direction whilst he was outside. 'I 'ad to climb froo a winda to get someone to give me a lighta.' Michael seemed positively thrilled with himself that he had achieved such a feat.

I bloody knew it.

'Michael!' My tone was half disappointment and half amusement at his act of sheer defiance and roguishness. 'You're supposed to have given up.'

'I know. I 'ave, Philip.' Michael chuckled. 'I needed to go outside and get some fresh air.'

I laughed with him. 'I don't think smoking a fag qualifies as fresh air!'

Michael stood by the big window in front of me, and chuckled as he stared outside. I lay on my bed and I could see past him and we could both see many other structures that made up the expanse of the hospital. Most notably, I saw the building below us that was a couple of stories lower than our block and it stretched out as far as a football pitch. What held Michael's attention as his laughter died down, was the roof. The cladding was made up of profiled copper sheets that had settled to a bright green colour through patination. I could tell Michael was fascinated by it – he seemed in a state of hypnosis by it.

'That's some roof down there,' I said, not sure if my words would break his trance.

'Yeah, it is. I'm a roofah int I, Philip?' He turned as he responded, and the magic spell was broken.

'Oh right. Nice one. What sort of roofs do you do?' Up until now I had been reluctant to ask about work, as terribly judgemental as it sounds. I'd resigned to the fact that Michael (when it came to employment status) was more likely to live off benefits than to be CEO of Iceland with unlimited bags for life as a perk.

'Anyfin'. Tilin', slate, anyfin' really.'

'That is handy to know, because I'm waiting for a guy I know to come round and do a bit of roofing for me at my house. He's been a bit busy...' It wasn't a lie - about a friend in the background being lined up to put a pitched roof over an old flat felt roof - but I didn't seriously consider Michael as a late substitution. From what I had observed of Michael, he did not look well enough to be carrying out any manual labour and certainly not up a bloody ladder.

Michael barely let me finish my sentence. 'I'll do it for ya, Philip.' The grin paused for a moment of seriousness, as his eyes widened and twinkled. He truly meant it. 'Yeah. If you get the materials and that, I'll knock it up for ya. I'll do it for free an all. Yeah, yeah, don't worry abaht it, I'll do it when I get outta 'ere.'

I could tell he was deadly serious about the offer, and I found myself at an uncomfortable fork in our relationship. Why had I even mentioned this? If I declined, I would have bound to cause offence as I would have effectively turned down a week's worth of the man's labour - for free! But, if I was to accept, there was every chance that I would have that man in my life, forever! He would get to know everything about me like where I lived, my phone number, what the rest of my family looked like, how good I made tea, everything.

I tried to match his enthusiasm about *our* new project as I was genuinely touched by Michael's generosity, and yet at the same, I attempted a tone that intended to play the whole thing down. I didn't want to give Michael any impression that it was a potential go-er.

'That is very kind of you. Thanks. You'll have to give me your number and if my mate lets me down, I'll give you a shout,' is what I said.

Michael was not one to give up, like a dog with a bone, he came back with, 'If you get the materials for us, I'll get it done for ya. Do ya a good job I will, Philip.'

'OK. Well, I won't bin my mate just yet. He did promise to help me out, but if he doesn't show up before the weather turns bad maybe we should sort something out.' My response felt like more repetition, and I hoped that Michael would realise that we could be stuck in a perpetual loop where he'd keep making an offer to fix my roof and my response would continue to be a maybe.

Fortunately, Michael seemed to be content with how we had left the roof situation, although I was surprised that he hadn't forced his phone number on me, or worse, asked for mine. He had turned back to the sight of the green roof out of the window.

As he stared out, the chuckles returned. 'Me and the boys would love to 'ave a go at that roof. We'd strip that bare in no time, Philip. Make a fortune on all dat metal.' His grin and daft nod worked overtime.

The penny dropped. Maybe I had been slower than a sloth walking up an icy hill with slippers on, but at least I got there in the end. It had suddenly dawned on me that my new friend, Michael, was a pikey, a gyppo. He was a traveller, or, as Viz readers might recall, a thieving gypsy bastard.

Jesus Christ on a trike.

Until that revelation, I just thought he was some grubby bloke that lived in a poor part of Langley with his young family and didn't have much of an education to better his lifestyle. My ignorance and my bigotry raged up to the surface. I didn't even realise gypsies got ill and went to the same hospital as us *town folk*.

Of course, how incredibly naïve of me to think they all lived in caravans. All the little things that Michael had told me started to add up - like the huge funerals for his parents, his appearance, the way he spoke, even his name. I felt a bit tricked - he wasn't classic Irish Traveller, and maybe it was the lack of a thick Irish accent that had prevented ignorant me from solving an easy mystery straight away.

I'd never had a gypsy friend before. I'll clarify that, I'd never even spoken to a gypsy before. Or if I had, it had been one or two sentences such as, 'No, I don't want any knives sharpened.' Or, 'No thank you, I'll jet-wash my own drive.' I'll be honest, I felt highly intimidated when they were out and about. Usually, they kept themselves to themselves and I've been more than happy to play along with that at a perfectly safe distance. We could always tell when they turned up at a restaurant or at a pub by the way they dressed, the volume of their accents, but mostly by the way they behaved to each other. I always considered them unpredictable, lawless, and untouchable by the police and they seemed to have no awareness of the personal space of others. Back at their homes I had seen them let their dirty, noisy kids run around outside, naked from the waist down, and witnessed them throw all sorts of things (tyres mainly) onto a bonfire, guarded by an Alsatian tethered by a thick bit of rope to an open caravan door. They left all sorts of mountainous shit behind whenever they were forced to leave the random car park or wherever they pitched up in the first fucking place...

Woah!

I needed to stop my awful, ugly rant right there.

People, just like me, with our bigoted views, gave them a bad name. Do-as-you-likey was one example. As the realisation of Michael's heritage sank in, I became ashamed of how I was so guarded in my attitude towards an entire community of people. Tyson Fury, the world heavyweight boxing champion, had done a superb job to highlight that last form of *acceptable* racism. The Gypsy King had spoken about how some shops and particularly pubs still put signs up and turned away people from the travelling community, and it seemed to go unchallenged throughout Britain. Well, I came to appreciate that that group of people were exactly that - people. Not the most profound statement ever made, but I needed to say it.

Michael, in so many ways, was just like me. I could tell that his love for his family was paramount, and it was evident that he was prepared to do whatever it took to be able to provide for them. I couldn't help but like someone that showed such open love for their family. Maybe he went about things in an unconventional way compared to 99% of the population, but his ultimate objective, to love and care for his family, was the same as mine. Then, to add a cherry on top, I looked at Michael and witnessed his generosity. He barely knew me, in fact, I was sure he would have regarded me as he would everyone else outside of his community (I don't think I was wrong to assume that prejudice was a two-way street most of the time) and yet he wanted to help fix my leaky roof. It wasn't in my nature to offer myself to anyone like he had – and that included people that were close to me that I cared about, let alone strangers.

Unabashed, Michael carried on with his stories of the many scrapes that he and his gang had got themselves into. It was all a big laugh to him. It seemed that Michael always avoided getting arrested by the police as they broke into various premises and took whatever they could carry. The common theme was that every time a security guard or the police turned up, Michael would play hide-and-seek and wait for the heat to fade away and then he would sneak out, untouched. Of course, the boys that always got caught would never grass, so the 'successful' pattern continued ad infinitum. I let Michael entertain me, uninterrupted, as he retold his adventures. The way he told each incident was child-like and I liked that he trusted me enough to openly discuss how he broke the law. Obviously, there were victims in those crimes, the thefts were always from a business or vacant property and the fights that sometimes accompanied the trespassing were with the authorities. Michael seemed to think it was all perfectly acceptable. I listened and, because Michael was so animated and funny, I would punctuate his stories with encouragement such as a 'Wow' or a 'No way'. We bonded, and the fact that I didn't have anything like an equivalent tale to share didn't really matter. I decided that Michael was good company to have around, if only to steal bite-sized chunks out of the mass of time we were both sentenced to.

The conversation with Michael had given me some much-needed light relief and, rather than wallow in the misery of my situation, we chatted about all sorts of topics. When it came to things that were important to me (family), Michael wasn't any different to me. Michael knew right from wrong; it was just that sometimes he had to cross the line to provide for the family that he loved more than anything else in the world. The difference was that I didn't have to cross the line – I guessed that was where privilege came into the equation.

I had a further opportunity to burn off a further ninety minutes as I watched Wales v Denmark in the last 16 of the Euros. I loved football, and I absolutely loved tournaments like the Euros and the World Cup. When I asked him, Michael said that he never really watched football. I conceded that I would have to watch the match on the small (slightly cracked) screen on my phone. There may have been a TV room for us patients to congregate in, but I hadn't found it and I hadn't bothered to ask anyone either because, quite frankly, I preferred to watch football on my own. The exception being big, noteworthy games. There was an exceptional game on the horizon that everyone in the know was aware of. England were due to play Germany, our biggest rival, on Tuesday. No fucking way was I going to be stuck in that hospital ward, forced to watch that huge match, on a tiny phone screen, when I should be at home with my family. I needed to be free to scream at the TV from the comfort of my sofa, with an ice-cold beer (or a proper cup of tea) in my hand...and a target had formed in my head.

Let's get all those tests done tomorrow, possibly Monday if there was to be nobody about at the weekend, and then I had to get home for Tuesday, nicely in time, for the England v Germany kick-off. Target set. I was going to do everything I possibly could to make sure that I was home for that biggie. What could stop me?

Nothing, that's what.

I had one more phone call to make that day. Tony, a Project Manager that worked with me on one of our sites. Just six weeks earlier he had been diagnosed with prostate cancer and, incredibly, he had returned to work after a successful operation to remove the offensive gland. He was lucky enough to have keyhole surgery and it had all been covered by his private healthcare insurance and apart from the complication of blood in his piss, the whole episode had gone relatively well. Tony's attitude had been remarkably positive, and he was completely focussed on making a full recovery as quickly as he could. I found Tony to be an inspiration. Very brave and ridiculously frank and open when he spoke about things associated with his trouser department. It was good that I felt I had an ally that understood exactly what sort of hurdles I might have to negotiate.

I think Tony was taken aback when I told him what I had been through over the previous 24-hour period. I explained what I could, but I couldn't fill in the blanks for the parts that he quizzed me on. Early days, mate, early days. Tony was supportive, realistic and he said all the right things with regards to the practicalities that related to work issues. He wasn't my line manager but he said he'd make all the calls on my behalf so I could concentrate on the speediest of recoveries. Tony knew our conditions were similar and yet very different, but he was confident that the doctors and the specialist teams would get me through everything – just as they had done for him. He told me to call him if there was anything on my mind and he said he would be there for me all the way. He bolstered me with his advice, all the while with his own bag of piss strapped to his leg, as he recovered from his operation that had stolen the functionality of his genitals. I thanked Tony as much as I could and was grateful that I did have someone at the end of a phone that understood the fears I had and, more importantly, he knew all about the terror I would face in the near future.

I felt better after that call with Tony. It was no-nonsense, positive, realistic, and full of hope, which was something I was grateful for. Afterwards, I watched the football, even though it was a pain because I had to crane my neck around to see the tiny screen. I had to place the phone on the thick plastic dado rail on my back wall. It had to be angled awkwardly because I needed to have the phone plugged in at the same time, otherwise, that woeful battery would let itself die on me. There was also plenty of banter within the WhatsApp groups which also helped distract me from my awful day. When it came to the football, Wales never got going, but if anyone was to smash the Welsh 4-0, I was glad it was the Danish. Everyone had adopted them as their second team after Christian Eriksen fell to the ground midway through the first half of a previous match with a cardiac arrest. At the time, I could not believe what I had watched, but all the Denmark players stood in a circle around their fallen teammate, faced outwards and made a shield for the paramedics as they fought to save Eriksen's life. 2021 had been a bizarre period for football in general, and it seemed that every week there was at least one game that had to be stopped whilst ambulance crews were called into action to save the life of someone in the crowd. What was doubly strange in that Denmark-Finland game was that it happened to a fit, young footballer. I didn't get sucked into conspiracy theories, but there was a hell of a lot of incidents happening all over the place at that particular time.

The banter between my friends seemed to stop when the match did, and I guessed they needed to get back to their normal lives. Probably had dishes to do and bins to put out. I would have loved to have been at home, with a dishwasher to load and to have important shit like recycling plastic containers to worry about.

Instead, the only things that got recycled were the words of that doctor. Neuroendocrine tumour. On my pancreas.

Oh, fuck it.

Maybe, because time had completely stopped earlier, the day had seemed extra-long. So much had happened. There was way too much to absorb. I was grateful that shock was there to protect me from all the frightening things that had gone on. I was exhausted physically, mentally and emotionally. I'd never known a day like it in my life. I sent a message to Ali to say that I felt tired, but I was well, and was turning in for the night. I took a last visit to the bathroom to brush my teeth and have a wee. I remained disappointed that my bowels still refused to shift anything, and I was worried that if my guts didn't start doing their job soon, it might be a reason for the authorities to say I would not be allowed home.

Yes, I could message Ali or the kids, or WhatsApp the guys, and if

I wanted to, I was sure I could have a chat with Michael, yet despite having all those people around, I'd never felt so sad and lonely.

Easy Like Sunday Morning

I slept well. Or to be more precise, during the extended times I wasn't awake, I slept well. It gave me the chance to catch up on some of the sleep I'd lacked over the previous two nights. Because I was still plumbed into the drips for the antibiotics throughout the night, I couldn't sleep on my side like I had since, well, since I can remember. I didn't want to crush the tubes or dislodge them and therefore I had to give the old – *lie back and think of England* – another try. The machinery and the alarms still made a racket but at least my inmates behaved themselves. I didn't hear the cries and screams like I had before. I worked out that I had enjoyed about four and a half hours of decent enough sleep and then at about 3:30am I stirred, needed the toilet, and then when I came back to bed, I continued to lay fully conscious instead of finding sleep for those final couple of hours.

Even on Sundays, the morning activities started early, and my personal routine started just before 6am with more antibiotics and a nurse at my bed that wanted to check my observations. I knew the deal – thermometer under the tongue, oxygen saturation clip on the index finger and then the good old blood pressure cuff around the bicep. Good morning, Wexham Park Hospital.

It looked like it would be a warm, sunny June day again. The roller blinds could not prevent the power of the early morning sun, and our closest star glowed through the fabric to light up our bay. The lit-up blinds reminded me of Michael's eyes when he got excited about something he cared about. I loved the summer and when I could feel the season fulfil its obligations, it helped to put me in good spirits. I exchanged some early morning text messages with Ali. As I suspected, she had slept less than me because she did more than enough worrying for both of us. Lydia had slept in with her mum again and Ali sent me a photo of her fast asleep. Although it was only a photo, I always loved to see my children asleep.

I enjoyed a very successful trip to the bathroom. I managed a shower. It wasn't anything like a wash in the comfort of my own home, but it made me feel surprisingly refreshed. Ali had brought me some shower gel and a towel in the baby pink bag, and it felt like I had washed away the sickness out of my hair and off my skin. I completed the rest of my usual routine and then made a decision that helped me ditch the notion that I was ill or some sort of victim - I boycotted the hospital gown.

I came out of the bathroom with my navy trackie bottoms and sported a clean blue T-shirt, just like I would have done if I'd been at home. If I hadn't been betrayed by the sight of all the cotton swabs from all the blood tests, and the cannulas in both arms, anyone would have thought I was just a visitor. I certainly did not look like one of the many gowned inmates.

Once back on my bed (ON not IN, I hasten to add), I didn't have to wait long before the man with the breakfast trolley came our way. I seemed to have evolved into one of Pavlov's dogs, as I heard the clang of the meal-time bell first, then the clank of crockery and cutlery before I saw the man himself. I discovered that I had an appetite. Saturday had been a day of sickness, vomiting and recovery, although I had accepted a cup of white coffee and a digestive biscuit in the evening around 6pm. That had been it when it came to any notable nutrition. The nausea had fizzled away, and the mystery infection had lifted and it gave way to allow familiar hunger pangs to remind me that it was about time I stuffed my face.

When asked what I would like to eat, I couldn't decide between toast or porridge, so I ordered both with a cup of tea. I reached over and pulled the tray-on-wheels over my waist and lay there, legs outstretched and it all felt remarkably comfortable. I was happy to look forward to the culinary delights served up from the hospital kitchen. Whenever anyone had asked me if I'd rather have the good news or the bad news, I'd normally have asked for the bad news first, so that we all end on that positive, feel-good note. Delayed gratification as they say. I felt so optimistic, I couldn't imagine breakfast serving up any bad news.

I thanked the breakfast trolley guy as he carefully loaded up my tray with goodies. I had declined the extra sugar on my bowl of porridge (a non-diabetic diagnosis would have meant a yes to the sugar) and I attacked it first as I wanted to eat it before it got too cold. The toast looked like it may have been on the guy's trolley for a while, so another two minutes wasn't going to affect the peak performance of that dish – the porridge had to go first. To be blunt, it was, without doubt, the worst porridge I've ever eaten in my entire life. I was pretty sure that only those near death, through starvation, or utter pigs (like me) would have finished the bowl. After one taste Goldilocks, the little diva, would have chucked the bowl against the big window opposite in disgust. Somehow, the porridge had become colder than room temperature. Somehow, it had become so lumpy that it achieved the same consistency as cold and lumpy mashed potato. Porridge should really taste of porridge rather than wet cardboard. I wrestled with myself and ended up convinced that I needed the energy that I believed hid within the elements of the mystery porridge, and so, I reluctantly forced it down. I did not shout out, *I'm A Celebrity Get Me Out of Here!* And, even though I completed the trial, no diminutive Geordies offered me a yellow star to take back in exchange for my campmates' dinner either. Fortunately, the portion size was not big. After I had gone through the motions, the porridge sat there as a heavy blob in my stomach. At least the toast, I reasoned, could offer up some flavour.

Incredibly, the toast matched the porridge for quality.

As suspected, it too was below room temperature. I peered down forlornly at one slice of bread that was neither white nor brown. It was a hybrid that adopted the very worst features from both parents. An anaemic, mottled, beige appearance. To mask the taste of the bread, they had given me a foil wrapped packet of Country Life butter (could the NHS even afford Country Life?) that I tried to warm up in my hands before I attempted to spread it. Now, I have held objects that have been at a temperature of zero degrees, but never in my life have I held anything that was at zero Kelvin. I guessed that objects at absolute zero on my breakfast trolley had probably been the reason why anything within a mile radius (or on the tray at least) was below room temperature. I was pleasantly surprised that the foil-clad cuboid didn't burn my palms like when doctors used liquid nitrogen to burn off a troublesome verruca. I unwrapped the butter and, armed with the bluntest knife I'd held since becoming an adult, made a pathetic attempt to spread the frozen lump on to the toast.

I fully expected to rip the toast to shreds as I battled with the solid state of the butter, but no, the butter stayed as one piece and just rolled over and over across the toast like a recklessly driven Mini in a stunt scene. There was no way that the butter was going to beat me, so I divvied it up into 5 equal(ish) slices and noted that I may as well have used the handle of the knife, since the blade was so dulled. Just a few minutes prior, before porridge-gate, when I was happy and optimistic about the up-and-coming free brekkie, I had selected marmalade over jam when asked. I was pleased to see that they hadn't cocked up the marmalade (alright – it was in a little pre-made plastic pot) and I even managed to apply the sticky blobs relatively evenly because the child-safe knife was not a limiting factor.

Nearly done, I rotated the toast on an angle and cut the toast into two triangles, as bread always tasted better in triangles. Only joking. I'd still be there now – I couldn't get that pathetic knife to cut anything! It had no chance against the toughness of the hybrid toast. I left it as one piece, sod it, presentation be damned.

I experienced a hint of sympathy for the knife when I finally bit into the toast. It was like I'd bit into an offcut of leather. Even a machete would have struggled to make a cut in that record-breaker. My teeth made an impression in the surface, but that was it. My jaws would've needed hydraulic help to break the miraculous fibrous bonds of the bread. I did the only thing I could and held the toast in my teeth and ripped the rest away with my stronger right arm. After at least double the amount of chewing and double the amount of saliva normally required, I managed to swallow that first bite. The tanginess of the marmalade overpowered the flavours of the salty butter and the extremely bland bread. Like Bear Grylls in survival mode, I made sure I got that nutrition inside me.

I almost forgot the good news. The tea was alright.

Sunday, Bloody Sunday

They came to collect my tray, and anyone would have thought that I must have really enjoyed it because there wasn't much left. I thanked the catering lady, and she handed me two menus. One for lunch and one for dinner (or tea to anyone born north of the Watford Gap).

Undeterred from the breakfast experience, I checked out the menus. The catering lady encouraged me to order early, and so I did. I felt like I'd missed out on a full-English, so I opted for the All-Day Breakfast, and she wrote it down on her pad, with tea as my drink. I also ordered a little pot of vanilla ice cream as a pudding. Then we sorted out the evening meal and, because it was Sunday, I asked for the roast chicken because it came with vegetables, roast potatoes, and gravy. Finally, because it was the dessert I would ask for if I was on Death Row, I selected fruit crumble with custard to finish off a fantastic Sunday meal. I say 'fantastic' because the pictures on the menu looked mouth-watering. I hoped that the joker that had thrown breakfast together only had an early two-hour shift on a Sunday, and the real chef would be in place for the rest of the day.

I killed time as I read Richard Osman's 'The Thursday Murder Club' that I had been given as a present the previous Christmas. I enjoyed it, the pace was racy – a good old-fashioned page-turner. Then, as I turned over to read page 34, a secret message waited for me. Ali loved her Post-It notes: -

I love you so much,
Mr Gorgeous.
Love from your Wifey
xx Ali xx

A lovely little surprise that brought a smile to my face. I understood the Page 34 reference. It was *my* number and the family knew it. It was no coincidence that the book I had just finished referred to the exact same number throughout. Every time Walter Payton's family saw the number 34 – they thought of him. Thirty-Four was Walter's number as well.

Just to confirm, 34 was the best number, there's no contest.

I put the book down for a while because Michael was on the move, with his carrier bag that contained individual fun bags of his bodily juices, and we fired up another chat. I asked him what delicacies he had selected from the not-particularly-extensive breakfast menu. I knew that he'd at least tried eating as they forced the hospital soup down his throat yesterday and he, slowly but surely, slurped his way through it. That morning, he was happy to report that he had enjoyed a bowl of Rice Krispies. Difficult for the bastard in the kitchen to cock-up that meal. Michael then asked me if I knew what the writing on the board behind us meant. My *NBM* had been wiped from existence, but Michael had *SFD* below his name. I was clueless and admitted defeat.

'No idea,' I said. 'They did have a note above my name that said I wasn't allowed any food, but I've got nothing there now. Maybe it is something to do with food or medication. We'll ask someone when they come by.'

'OK. Fanks, Philip.' Michael seemed grateful even though I didn't solve his query. 'I'm no good at readin' ya see. I got kicked out of school when I was little.' His shame was evident, yet it had been diluted somewhat, probably from the need to explain himself many times in the past. He seemed to have come to terms with it.

'I ayted ve teachas. Got expelled when I was fifteen, Philip.'

Michael began one of his stories and his mood changed from the sadness associated with his illiteracy to the excitement of the opportunity to explain to someone new, the history behind his exclusion from school.

'When I was in Year 7, vhere was this kid that fawt he was well 'ard.' Michael's smile shone through his stubbly face. 'Anyway, I got 'old of one of vem pens wiv the metal ends and I waited for 'im. Then I see 'im, right. In the corridor. 'E said somefin' to me and I just jumped 'im. Stabbed him right in the top of 'is 'ead wiv' the pen.' Michael seemed to be waiting for some sort of reaction from me before he carried on.

'Well, I can see why they wouldn't like that sort of thing in the school.' My words were serious, but my tone was laced with a hint of amusement. I mean, the story was shocking, and there was clearly at least one victim here but, as I have explained before, I made a decent chameleon and I thought it might be best to humour my gypsy friend rather than be his next reason why he'd got himself thrown out of a tax-funded establishment.

Michael's voice raised up from his standard growl to a much higher, excited pitch, 'There was blood EVERYWHERE!'

I didn't say anything.

'It was all ovah the walls. The floor. All over ME!'

The excitement in Michael's tone stayed. He showed no remorse. It seemed that he'd probably do the same thing again if someone invented a time machine for him to have a second chance. Again, there was a natural pause as Michael waited for my response, but I just looked back at him, dumbfounded. I wondered where his tale would go.

'He didn't die or nuffink, Philip.' Michael's voice had settled back down to his gravelly best and he looked away and down. Possibly a flicker of remorse.

Nope. He remembered something else and couldn't contain himself, and the eyes and grin were on maximum brightness. 'He squealed so LOUD!' Michael clearly loved his story. 'You've nevah eard nuffink' like it, Philip. Oh man. SO LOUD!'

I let him finish. I guessed his story might have got more gruesome and bloodier each time he retold it.

The fire of Michael's rendition seemed to burn out. He returned to his quieter, almost reflective state. 'Anyway. Ve teachas ayted me, didn't vey. Vey chucked me out. I nevah went back.'

'It's a shame you never learnt to read though.' And as I said these words, I had a sudden flashback to the scene in Shawshank Redemption where Andy Robbins' character taught one of his prison friends to read. For a split second I thought – shit, am I destined to spend the rest of the week teaching my travelling friend the alphabet?

'Yeah,' Michael agreed. 'I get by vough, Philip. My missus elps. She's pretty good at vat sort of fing.'

I didn't think he could blame his illiteracy on leaving school at fifteen. If they'd expelled him at five, possibly, but he really should have nailed it well before he started secondary school. Clearly this chap had other issues that stopped him from reading like any average Joe. If we did end up stuck together for a long spell, maybe I could *teach* Michael and hopefully find it to be the perfect way to kill time. If anything needed to be stabbed in the head, it was the undetermined time between now and getting home.

'Well, God bless the wives!' I cheered, and I raised a plastic cup of water.

Michael raised his plastic cup in unison and my toast proved a good way to end Michael's bloody tale.

Although it was the day of rest for the majority of the world, there were many good people that were at work. Normally, I would have been at home having a perfectly chilled (lazy) day. My routine would have started off with a shower and a shave, I would have thrown on some comfy clothes and then gorged on a fried egg sandwich (with equal amounts of bright yellow yolk and bright red ketchup applied around the corners of my mouth) all washed down with a tasty cup of hot tea. Then, after I had cleaned up my chops, I would have pushed on with painting Pelé with Judge Judy on in the background, to keep me company until the rest of the family finally woke up to join me. That particular Sunday, unfortunately, did not shape up to be in my top ten of best ever Sundays.

Forty hours in, and I had already become used to the relentless routine of blood tests, finger prick tests, blood pressure tests, temperature tests, intravenous drips of antibiotics, covid tests and now there was still the daily injection in my thigh to stop blood clots. I did challenge the injection once again - as I hadn't had any surgery and now it was known that there was no plan for me to have any surgery. The nurse told me that *everyone* had this, regardless to how active the patients were. I complied and took the shot like a good boy. I was determined to be an obedient patient, to be released early for good behaviour.

A different nurse arrived at my bed. She seemed about the same age as me and yet I got an air that she hadn't done her job for long. She came across quiet and, in my opinion, bordered on the unfriendly. We struggled with small talk because English wasn't her preferred language, so I let her get on with the checks she had come over to do. She put the blood pressure cuff on my right arm. I stopped her because, up until that moment, the other nurses had used the opposite arm to where my cannula was sited. After I'd had several of those bloody things jabbed into me, the cannula half-way up the inside of my lower right arm seemed to have behaved itself. She told me flatly that it wouldn't make any difference.

She was wrong.

Very wrong.

As the blood pressure cuff inflated around my bicep, I experienced a searing pain between the cannula and my elbow – it hit me instantly. The sting felt like a red-hot needle had pierced my arm up my vein, through it, and into the muscle. As the cuff continued its squeeze, like a boa constrictor, the pain accelerated exponentially, and the heat intensified. The sensation of a metal needle inside me increased as it seemed to be expanding, and I swear that imaginary needle fucking grew! It felt like the vein in my arm physically stretched beyond its expected physical properties. My agony had shot off the pain-Richter scale. I had to stop it. I seriously believed my vein was going to explode.

'ARRRGGGH! Ow! Shit! Stop!' I shrieked, as I reached out to release the cuff.

'What?' the nurse responded but she was way behind me.

The machine was automatic, it did what it was supposed to do. It squeezed the fuck out of my arm, that's what it did. It continued to force air into the cuff, and with nowhere for the air to go, it persisted with the compression of my arm even further. There was no pain shut off valve. As far as the machine was concerned, it had only just begun its simple program.

I was frantic and I scrambled for the Velcro straps that held the cuff in place. The nurse finally realised why I screamed out in distress and, thankfully, poked at a button on her machine.

The pumps that forced out the air stopped instantly, and the relief was immediate. The cuff began to release its vice-like grip, but the pain remained where my arm had been damaged. Fortunately, as with most injuries, my body was already on the case and it sent out some natural endorphins to battle the agony, and the panic of a burst blood vessel had gone. The emergency was over as quickly as it had started. What was left was a fucked-off me that now owned a very sore arm, that showed the evidence of the damage caused. I saw the line of my expanded vein exactly where it had been breached under the skin. An evil-looking red and purple bruise told the story. My breathing returned to normal from the panic mode it had been in. I was grateful that the machine had been shut off when it had, because everything could have been so much worse. A hot flush came over me, like an aftershock. Shit, I thought, I might be sick again.

The nurse did not say sorry. She seemed annoyed about the whole episode. Had she appeared apologetic, I may have tried to not make her feel any worse. Instead, because I felt sorry for myself, I firmly told her that what happened truly hurt me and reminded her that I had suggested using my other 'free' arm. We were never going to get along, and she maintained that it shouldn't matter which arm she used and then she moved around to the other side of my bed and strapped up my other arm to complete her visit. That test went as well as those tests go, but the reading was high, no doubt due to the stress I'd experienced. She left and there was no goodbye from either of us.

I was left alone for the next hour, which suited me just fine. I had expected the doctors any moment, as I had been told they would do their rounds from 10am and we were about to approach high noon. It was Sunday, so maybe trading hours at the hospital were completely different. To cheer me up, I heard the double clang of the meal-time bell. I almost felt a primary school urge to line up, like we were being treated like children or simpletons. I could laugh off those thoughts, some of the patients here probably needed the bell to help structure their plans, their thoughts and all their ambitious dreams of what they could achieve that day within the great walls of the hospital.

The All-Day Breakfast came my way. It was more edible than the meal I had been served at first light. My grumpy mood had improved a little - at least *most* of the fry-up was warm. I managed to camouflage the majority of the less favourable tastes and smells with baked beans and ketchup. There was scrambled egg (dry but edible with moisture from the said ketchup); the sausage was cheap and tasteless (but at least it had been cooked and therefore acceptable); the bacon was hard and greasy (and almost acceptable – it would've made a better shoe horn); the toast was plain white (I could actually butter and cut it which was a vast improvement from the morning show); but I left the black pudding (I simply couldn't trust it).

Normally, when I lay on a bed and got the opportunity to eat a meal, it would be fantastic, especially when being treated at home. When it was my birthday or Father's Day, once in a blue moon, breakfast-in-bed felt like a real luxury. The truth was, I always found that whenever I ate a meal that way, it would border on the uncomfortable. I soon discovered that if I was to have every meal prostrate, it wouldn't take me long for the novelty to wear off. At the point of my second meal, I had already managed to get pissed off with the whole idea. Therefore, I tucked into my All-Day Breakfast whilst sat in my comfortable armchair like somebody that was fit and well. I had been able to lower the tray, so everything was to hand and, well, comfortable.

Whilst forking in a mouthful of toast that carried a little bit of everything, I looked up to see the group of doctors that had come to visit. It was the same Death Squad as yesterday. Mr D'Freitas as the Grim Reaper, flanked by his two junior reapers and a nurse. Superb timing yet again!

The female junior doctor had spotted that I was sat down and (almost) enjoying my lunch. Before they got the chance to commence their usual routine, she suggested to her fellow Death-Eaters that maybe they should come back until after I had finished my meal.

'Mmm, yes, yes,' D'Freitas seemed to agree with his protégé. He looked from her and back to me and said, 'Hello, Philip. Shall we come back after you are finished?'

I chewed on a mouthful of egg and bacon, so my response was to give them all a few nods. I thought it would best to spare them all a repeat performance of yesterday – I didn't want to spray the crowd with half-eaten food when I opened my mouth.

'OK, OK. We will come back and see you later,' he confirmed, and his troop followed him as he completed a U-turn and went to upset someone else. That someone wasn't Michael; he was already being seen by a completely different team.

They had done the right thing. It is one of my rules of life - *Never disturb someone who is eating a meal.*

I finished off the rest of my lunch (or was it breakfast?) and noted that the mug of tea was nowhere near as good as the one I'd had in the morning. Weak, milky and lukewarm. Still, with a full belly, my spirits continued to improve, and I was prepared to take on the world, or at least the world of Dr Death and his entourage.

As promised, the Doctors returned about fifteen minutes after their first attempt. I had finished my meal, which had ended with an unusual pot of ice cream. It did taste vaguely of vanilla but had the consistency of airy foam and, like the tea, was lukewarm. I dreamt of a perfect Mr Whippy 99, as I scraped out the last bits and consumed the vanilla-flavoured foam. The entire meal had been totally functional and not particularly enjoyable.

The nurse closed the curtains. Here we go again.

'Hello again, Philip. How are you feeling today?' Mr D'Freitas asked. He sounded like he wanted to keep things light.

I sensed (prayed) that he was not about to drop another grenade my way. 'Better than yesterday.' That had been my honest reply. I was normally respectful and friendly to our friends in the medical profession, but I couldn't help but act a touch frosty with D'Freitas.

It had nothing to do with what he said to me yesterday and all about the way he had said it or, to be more precise, the fact he couldn't wait for me to stop puking until he rendered his grave verdict. I wasn't one to shoot the messenger but if they were going to deliver that kind of message in a shitty way, then they probably deserved a slap.

'Good. We have looked at your tests from yesterday and you are responding to the antibiotics.' D'Freitas at least tried to be friendly, but he had a tough crowd (me).

I didn't let my guard down - maybe it was a tactic to soften me up.

'We are going to keep you here as we do have some other tests to do, hopefully this afternoon or possibly, Monday.'

'Oh. So, I can't go home today then? Can I go home and then come back here when you need me for the tests?' I just wanted to get home and I didn't care if they all thought I sounded desperate to get out of that bloody place because I WAS desperate.

'No, sorry. No. We can't work like that. Sorry. We must finish the antibiotics and we have to keep monitoring you.'

'OK. What tests?' I asked neutrally.

'There are some other blood tests we need to take to help us see how active this problem is and there are some further scans, a chest X-ray to make sure that we haven't missed out anything.' D'Freitas had returned to his robotic matter-of-fact mode, although he did, I detected, sound a little more upbeat. I think he found that part of his job difficult.

I had figured that tests and scans were what my immediate future was all about. I had discussed it with Chrissy, the Macmillan nurse, so I knew they hadn't finished with their prods and pokes. I had accepted that all of us needed to know what the spread of the disease was and how aggressive it was.

Aggressive.

That was quite the word. Aggressive as in hostile and destructive. Fucking marvellous.

I softened. Maybe if I was nice to these people then the results of the tests would be more favourable. I was prepared to try anything. I poked out an olive branch and gave an apology.

'Look, I'm sorry if I was rude yesterday,' I said to all the team that stared back at me. 'It's just that I was not expecting what you told me, and I was being sick and everything...'

'Yes. I was just telling you what I had to tell you.' D'Freitas had become defensive.

For a moment I thought I might let rip and give the insensitive robot a piece of my mind, but he carried on.

'Look, Philip. It is a lot to take in.' D'Freitas barely acknowledged my apology, and he certainly didn't follow suit with, '*I should have given you 5 minutes to wipe the vomit off your chops before I slapped the great news across your face.*'

Instead, he asked, 'Do you have any questions about anything we know at the moment?'

'Yes. Is this the real reason that I was diagnosed with diabetes a year ago? I mean, could this have happened back then, and I was mis-diagnosed?'

'That is something I can't comment on. But it is good that we have found this now, before it grows any bigger and causes more problems.'

I wasn't totally convinced. Yes, it was extremely lucky that the scan I had for something unrelated had picked up on it when it did. Imagine if it had been discovered six months later, when the tumour had doubled in size, strangling multiple blood vessels that caused excruciating pain and resulted in an ambulance ride with Ali sobbing her heart out next to me. *But* - on the flip-side - the local GP and the teams that had examined the blood from my MOT-style health check had figured my sugar levels were crap because of diabetes. Maybe they could have booked me in for a scan, you know, to make 100% sure. I guessed it was all about money and funding.

With a niggling doubt, I considered myself lucky. After all, I was a lucky guy.

'OK. Do you know how big this lump is? I don't think you said yesterday.'

'Yes. It is quite large.' D'Freitas had held his hands up between us and his thumbs touched each other and so did his index fingers. He couldn't have made a bigger circle without breaking contact with any of those four digits. His manner was chatty, like we were talking about how big the meat was in a Burger King Whopper.

Fucking Hell!

I don't know why, but I had assumed I had to deal with something the size of a boil on my pancreas. In fact, I didn't know how big my pancreas was – it looked like the tumour D'Freitas demonstrated was bigger than the organ itself.

'WHAT?!' I blurted out with my eyes wide in a display of how stunned I was. I couldn't hold back the fright. I leaned forward, 'SERIOUSLY?! That's big, isn't it?'

He looked taken aback from my outburst and his mood changed from chatty back to formal. He quickly closed the hole he had made with his hands, like a shutter in a camera, to about half the size. From Whopper to a handsome sized plum.

'Well, quite big yes.' He looked down at his adjusted hands. 'About 10 centimetres by about 7 point 6 centimetres.'

Automatically I converted it to inches, something like 4 inches by 3. Shit. It still sounded enormous. Bollocks. He didn't give a third dimension, but I guessed I was living with something proportional and blobby rather than a two-dimensional mini tortilla.

I emptied out whatever air remained in my lungs as an exasperated groan. The latest news headline felt like an immense knock back.

We looked at each other.

Was I terrified? No.

Why not? Shock and denial. Cheers guys, you never let me down.

What did I think then? As I considered the information I just felt thoroughly pissed-off. Annoyed that it had stopped my normality. How come I hadn't even physically felt such a huge object inside me?

'Please, try not to worry. We are going to look after you.' The doctor's words were genuine.

I might have appeared distant because I was. I wondered, what the fuck could they possibly do for me? Short term, cut out what they could, then untold rounds of chemotherapy (coupled with the associated sickness – what fun) in a vain attempt to delay the inevitable.

I would fight the good fight, as long as there was a glimmer of hope. If they were about to throw the word terminal into the mix, well, I didn't know what to think. I had been in a head-fuck the day before and that was nothing compared to the flat-spin I found myself in.

'The scans have confirmed that there is no blockage in your bowels, so that is some good news, but we saw some other things that we do need to check further.'

Jesus Herbert Christ, what now?

'Your prostate seems to be larger than it should be at your age, so whilst you are here, we want to have a check on that. Also, the neuroendocrine tumour has grown into the vessels and ducts around the spleen, and we have to be certain that the spleen and other organs in and around that area are not damaged. We can also see that you have some kidney stones, one of which is quite large, so we just need to work out exactly what all this means and what treatment is going to be best for you.'

It was no surprise to hear that they considered my prostate gland as *enlarged*. I'd only had GP confirmation up until then. I told the team that I was aware of my prostate situation and I felt comforted (rather than scared) that the team were going to delve deeper, and I'd soon find out if that was another major problem or not. Two birds, one stone and all that. *Do your tests,* I thought, *just get on with it.* I must have been desensitised to all the dozens of procedures that had happened or would happen because they probably could've got away with giving me a penile umbrella scrape test and I would have responded with a 'Whatever.'

I can't remember how the rest of the conversation went as my mind was elsewhere as I contemplated my fate and made plans for my final months. I do remember that I asked if I was to be moved to Hammersmith and was told that it was still a possibility, but we wouldn't know until after the weekend. OK, I thought, I think I've had enough of an update for one day. We all said our goodbyes and they turned and left me sat in my chair. The nurse thrust open the curtain so I could look out of the window, but she left the side curtain that separated me from Michael, and I was grateful for that. I did not want to speak to anyone.

The junior doctor, the female one, came back after just a few seconds.

Alright, I'll speak to her.

'Hi,' she said as she moved towards the right-hand side of my bed. 'I just wanted to see if you were OK after hearing everything.'

At last, praise the Lord, a half-decent bedside manner. Maybe it was her youth and lack of experience in the trenches and the delivery of terrifying news to patients was still a new thing, instead of a run-of-the-mill standard day at the office. No, it was a little more than that; I thought that she had started out as a doctor because she wanted to care for people in need.

'Hi. Er...yes, there is a lot to take in. Let me just say that I appreciate you could see I was eating before, and it was definitely the right call to let me finish. You can pass on that I was far from impressed with the doctor telling me all of that whilst I was being sick on the floor. It wouldn't have taken much to have given me five minutes.'

She apologised, yet it wasn't her fault. 'You're right. I'm really sorry about that.'

'Well, we've all learnt an important lesson, to never interrupt someone if food is going in, or worse, coming out.'

'Absolutely,' she agreed and I could tell from her scrunched up eyes that there was a smile under her mask.

I told her that I didn't have any other questions and she reassured me that if I did, she would be around all day, so if I needed to speak to someone, I just had to ask for her. She told me her name was Nicole.

'Great. Thank you.' I smiled gratefully as she departed. Her little PR exercise had worked on me. The battle would have many ups and downs – no doubt about it. I predicted a series of discoveries that would frighten anybody, followed by carefully considered remedies. Nicole represented the sensitive element of the team. I couldn't give a shit if D'Freitas proved to be an utter wanker, if he was brilliant and sorted me out, then I'd give the unsympathetic fucker the biggest hug I could.

Inmates

I realised that prison life - oops sorry - *hospital* life, was entirely structured around mealtimes, at least it was for me, punctuated by regular observations, the distribution of medication at appropriate times, and finally, the all-important visiting hours. After the doctors finished with their rounds, there was a void between the next event, which was scheduled to be my clandestine meet up with my family in the car park. It gave me an opportunity to connect with the other unfortunate souls that resided in Bay Number Four.

On Saturday, a sweet old gent named Reg had been discharged from Bed number 2 - the other side of Michael's bed. I had no idea what he had come in for, but he appeared to have been reasonably mobile for someone between 75 and 85 years old. He was tall and had a strong build, and he looked healthy from the outside. He came across pleasant and was cheery to all the staff, so I deduced that he had been clear of pain and distress. Even though I hadn't spoken to Reg, I was aware that he had been given the all-clear to be discharged that day. After I'd overheard the discharge news, I predicted that Reg would still have to wait about all day. I was proved right. They had given him the green light and told him that he was a free man (once the paperwork had been signed of course) at 10:30am. Reg, with an antique but functional Nokia, called his daughter to tell her the good news and she agreed to be on standby to pick him up (once the doctor had signed the right papers and the pharmacy had rustled up his medication).

Eleven hours later and Reg was still sat on the edge of his bed!

He dressed smartly, with trousers and a work shirt, like most men of that generation. He wore dark brown leather shoes, and he looked like he might be off to work had he been 20 years younger. He didn't make a fuss. Reg's holdall, which I bet was expertly packed like a person that had completed National Service, sat next to him, just as patiently. He had everything packed and ready to go, since the morning. Maybe the doctors had gone home and forgotten about signing Reg's discharge paperwork.

Finally. Finally! At nine o'clock on Saturday evening, they eventually handed over his release papers. He gratefully received it with the little bag of pills that the in-house pharmacy had rustled up and I saw that he was straight on the phone to his daughter. Twenty minutes later he was off, with a 'Thank you,' and a 'Cheerio' to all the nurses he could find on his way out. I liked Reg; he seemed like a proper gentleman.

Within minutes of his departure, a staff member had stripped the bed and new sheets had been tucked in to welcome a brand-new resident. Everyone had already moved on from Reg, the Gent; there was no time for sentiment. He had been fixed up, and was now on his way home, no doubt to be spoiled rotten by his devoted daughter and the rest of the family.

Or so I thought.

Just before I made my trip to the bathroom, Reg returned to Bay 4. In his haste to escape Colditz, the poor sod had forgotten his bag. He spent another ten minutes at least as he felt obliged to say even more *Thank yous* and *cheerios* to even more nurses. I would have been in a rage, but Reg stayed calm and dignified, and I really hoped, for his sake, that his 'Goodbye' was his final one.

That all happened the day before, and Reg's bed (it would always be Reg's bed to me) had become occupied by a distressed, tubby, Indian chap. He seemed to have spent much of his Sunday afternoon curled up on his side, and whenever someone passed by, he would cry out in pain. He was young, no older than 25, and alternated between bouts of either sleep or consciousness (but in a state of agitation) in equal 15-minute bursts.

Michael had taken his bag of juices for a walk. Which we both knew meant he had gone outside for a smoke. I carried on with my book and all would have been calm except that Raj, our new tubby inmate, continued to moan out loud. He must have reached a point where he could not stand the pain any longer - he pressed his alarm button.

Instead of a siren that would wake the dead, there was barely a noticeable *bing* that gently repeated itself every ten seconds. A light that flashed might have been more perceptible than the constant light that came on. The ward, no doubt the whole hospital, was on weekend staff and I thought that Raj might not get the help he wanted particularly quickly.

'Hello?!' I called out. 'Can someone come and help, please?' I was more annoyed than panicked. Annoyed that the alarm could mean someone was in genuine trouble. 'HELLO? Is there anybody there? We have an alarm going off!'

Nothing. I waited a further twenty seconds and still nobody came.

I repeated my shout to let anyone within earshot know that an alarm had been set off and then, deflated, I looked over to Raj. He was in a foetal position, curled up on his side, and I saw that he held his tummy. He was teary, anguished and obviously sounded the alarm because of his pain. I called over to Raj, 'Sorry, my friend. It looks like we're on our own.'

Raj stayed teary as he acknowledged me with two slow, sad nods.

He didn't look critical. My expert professional opinion confirmed that - from a dozen yards away. He appeared to be in the same degree of pain that he'd been in since he'd arrived two or three hours prior. Whatever was up with him, he needed to sweat it out, until help came.

Appendicitis, it was clear. Everyone with a painful tummy, especially when they were scrunched up like Raj, had appendicitis. I was confident that the doctors that were committed to save him would have considered the same diagnosis. We were all in the surgery ward, so it seemed a high probability that one of the operating theatres beneath us was about to get prepped up, ready to receive Raj to cut out his infected, odious appendix.

It had been several minutes but eventually a nurse did show up. I saw that she successfully calmed Raj. He must have been the same age as my eldest; early twenties. I noticed that no painkillers were given to him. It looked like the power of some care, love and attention, some words of comfort, and the contact from her touch on Raj's shoulder seemed to do the trick. The attentive nurse turned off the alarm, made sure Raj felt better, then left him to it. Busy times for the overworked, understaffed NHS.

Over on the far side of Bay 4 was Chris. He had hidden over in the opposite corner since I'd arrived on the Friday. He kept himself to himself, but I did see him every now and then, when he made trips to and from the bathroom. Chris was a good twenty years younger than me and was prepared to use technology to entertain himself, what I mean is, he permanently had Airpods jammed in his ears whenever I saw him. He was either on the phone or plugged in to listen to music or, sometimes, he watched a film on his tablet as he lay in bed. The Airpods were a permanent fixture no matter what he was up to. I considered him either unapproachable or, possibly, just unfriendly.

Chris gave the impression of someone that could make their hospital stay as comfortable as possible. Not only did he have his home cinema with him, but he also had his bathrobe and his sliders, and a designer washbag and I guessed that Chris did not have the same challenges I experienced whenever he used the bathroom - I bet he didn't dunk his smart gown in the toilet bowl. I'll admit that I was a bit of a dinosaur and I was never a fan of Airpods or headphones, even worse when I'd seen younger (always younger) work colleagues sat at their desks with coloured bits of plastic wedged into their heads. It made a statement of *I DO NOT WANT TO TALK TO ANYBODY*. They also reminded me of that scene in the film Something About Mary when Ben Stiller answered the door to Cameron Diaz straight after *relieving himself* to avoid going out with a *loaded gun*, so to speak. Those popular white Airpods looked like what Diaz assumed was hair gel hung from Stiller's right ear. I couldn't unthink the image, but at least the humour of it helped quash my distain against such unsociable bits of kit.

When I'd been on holiday, to a new place, I'd always felt like a fish out of water for those first few days. I guess all normal people did. Whenever I was in a hotel, I was never quite sure of *the deal* when it came to mealtimes and, come to think of it, all the other facilities, places, and routines. I resigned myself to make one schoolboy error after another. However, every other fucker I saw there seemed to know exactly what the craic was - they all looked like they'd been there for weeks. We only know we've got it sussed when we see the *newbies* arrive, and I could then chuckle to myself as they tried to tackle the little conveyor belt machine that made the toast. That bit of equipment took the average person at least ten attempts to master it. Once round left the bread barely warm, twice round meant it was burnt to a crisp.

If anyone had an air of, *I know the deal around here,* it was Chris. From a distance, he looked a similar height to me, although whereas I was a touch over 6 foot, Chris looked a smidgeon under. He was clean shaven, with dark hair slicked-back, with an overall smart appearance. He spoke well, and I got the impression he was a clever guy. Clever yet unapproachable. I figured that maybe Chris thought his three cell mates would be best kept at arm's length. I couldn't blame him if he did think that.

Confession time: I had always been a bit of an eavesdropper. I'd better qualify that. If there was nothing else better to distract me, I was nosey enough to listen in on a conversation that sounded interesting. If that was a sin then, Lord, strike me down. Sometimes, I couldn't help but be aware of other people's business, especially if they possessed a naturally loud voice that carried. As much as Chris spoke well and was articulate, he did have one of *those* voices that carried. Oh yes, I found out all about Chris' story.

Firstly, Chris had a son called Hector. Chris called his son Hecky, which was his shortened version that sounded just as annoying. Hecky was almost two years old and craved attention like no other toddler in the history of mankind. Hecky may have had a serious hearing problem because despite being told to be quiet or to calm down approximately a hundred times, he wouldn't do a fucking thing he was told. Chris got frustrated with Hecky over the phone, and he probably got equally frustrated with his son when they were at home together. Seven weeks before, Chris underwent a vasectomy. I wondered if Hecky was the main reason why Chris had chosen to go through with such a permanent contraception at his young age. Chris had used his private healthcare to facilitate the snip. There had been some complications and Chris' testicles had swollen up beyond belief. It sounded like an exaggeration, but several times I heard Chris tell each new doctor that one of his bollocks had resembled a tennis ball and the other was even worse, more like a cantaloupe melon. Chris was very vocal and therefore we all knew how incredibly sensitive his nuts were and how distressed he was with all the pain and discomfort he was in. I had noticed his gait whenever he made a trip to the bathroom - it was slow and tentative, because he obviously needed to protect those awfully painful balls.

On a different level, my ears had become awfully sensitive, too. If I heard the name Hecky once, I'd heard it a thousand times.

'Shush, Hecky... Yes, Hecky. HECKY! Get down from there Hecky. Shush, Hecky. HECKY! No, HECKY! Don't do that, Hecky. No Hecky. HECKY! Listen, Hecky. Stop that, Hecky. HECKY! HECKY? HECKY!'

As much as I pitied Chris for his infected gonads, the name Hecky had managed to get right on my tits.

Despite his son's name grating on me so badly, I took an interest in Chris' on-going bollock-based saga. The NHS were now picking up the slack after private healthcare had failed him. Even the most straight forward surgical procedure bore the threat of infection and since his operation, Chris had been in and out of hospitals and whenever he'd been sent home, he had been shipped back into hospital in a worse condition than before. The private practice was fine with operations but they couldn't cater for people that outstayed their allotted time with tricky complications. I made a mental note to walk over and have a dad-like chat with him, when the time was right, to make sure he got some decent compensation for the (pun intended) balls up. It seemed scandalous that a private practise could harm one of their paying patients in the first place and then expect the NHS to mop up the mess.

I heard Chris as he continued to Facetime his son. 'Hecky! Stop it, Hecky! Listen Hecky. Listen! Hecky! HECKY! Get mummy, Hecky.'

Mind you, as incredibly painful as Chris's infected balls sounded, it would be a small price to pay if it meant no more Heckys.

Poirot Minus Moustache

Someone had stolen my medicine.

I couldn't find my pills anywhere. I'd returned from the bathroom (still nothing solid to report) and the box had gone.

It was my Metformin, my diabetes medication that helped keep my blood sugar levels in check whilst my pancreas wasn't fully engaged - and it was the only box I had. I rummaged through all my belongings. I had to confess, my corner had got a bit messy, but all my things were within a two-metre radius from the centre of my bed. A further search, more intense than the man's look that had induced minor panic, still drew a blank. Damn it! I couldn't find them anywhere. I was certain that I had left them on my tray. I regretted the decision to leave everything so exposed whilst I went on my jaunt, but nothing else had gone walkies – just the pills. The only thing of any real value was my phone, and that was still there. Who the hell would have taken the drugs?

I exchanged some text messages with Ali, just in case she had accidentally taken them home with her at the end of our visit last night. She'd taken some of my used underwear back home and maybe, just maybe, they'd got caught up in the bundle. No luck. Ali's reply confirmed the worst. They were gone for sure.

Some bloody thieving git had taken them!

I was ashamed to admit that I put two and two together and came up with an accusation I am not proud of. I concluded, after a far from thorough investigation, that the crime must have been committed by my gypsy neighbour. Michael had no alibi and, apart from the occasional nurse, he was the only one that knew exactly when I was away from my bed. He had *previous* as he'd disclosed his history of larceny the day before. I deduced that he probably wouldn't have even thought through the consequences. I bet he didn't have a clue what Metformin was and probably just took them just because they were drugs. He probably wanted to sell them to a junkie mate once he was out of hospital.

He was prime suspect and all I had to do now was to find enough evidence to nail the fucker.

I wondered if the ward had any CCTV. The ceiling, that I was familiar with having spent two nights staring up at it, was full of all sorts of lights, emergency lights, vents, sensors, sprinkler heads, alarms, the lot, but I didn't think there was anything that looked like a CCTV camera to me. I bet they had them in the corridors though; fat lot of good they'd be to help crack the case.

Michael had left the scene. Conveniently he had absconded to go outside for one of his regular fag breaks, even though he'd quit smoking. I casually walked past his bed and as I did, I spied over his things to see if my little beige and light green cardboard box was being held captive there. No. Of course it wasn't. Michael had squirreled the merchandise away like the true expert he was. I sauntered back to my corner, empty-handed. I really didn't want the situation to get out of hand. It might seem negligible, but I was going to have to tell someone.

It wasn't long before the nurse that had busied around all morning came by. Awkward as it was, I had to tell her. Even if we couldn't track down the stolen pills, I would need some new ones to accompany my evening meal.

'Hi,' I said, as I looked up from my armchair. 'I'm really sorry, but I seem to have lost my pills. They were here on my tray, but they've gone.'

'Oh, sorry. I should have told you. I saw them there and we do not allow medication to be left out.' She pointed to a lockable metal box that was fixed to wall behind me, above my head. 'They're locked up in that safety box.'

'Oh,' I said. I felt like a right pilchard. 'Thanks.'

'I'll go and get the key for you. You can put other valuables in there as well.' She turned and left to get the key for me.

I thanked her once again and was left there with the mystery of the drugs snatch solved. She also left me to stew over my guilt over my unnecessary accusation – which sat with me, like an embarrassing bag of shit.

Michael came back from his venture outside in a noticeably buoyant mood. The tubes and various bags did not bother him at all. He seemed to get better and better every hour. I wouldn't put it down to the fags, but the activity of him getting up and about, and his optimistic demeanour looked like they had helped Michael's recovery.

'It's Sunday!' He beamed at me.

I smiled back, and I hoped my tale of my unfounded allegation of drug theft would never reach him. 'Yes, it is!'

'We need to smuggle in a Mackie's, Philip.' His tongue poked out a tiny amount, and he almost licked his lips as he referred to his favoured take away of choice.

'You know what, you probably could get away with that in here. Although, I'm not so sure you are allowed to eat something like that just yet.' As usual I was getting carried away with Michael's infectious enthusiasm and then I appeared to smack it down with the fist of common sense. 'Did you order some food off the menu for later?'

'Sort of. They're still givin' me the soft food or somefing today.' His child-like sadness clouded over him.

'Shame. Sunday should be a roast dinner day, right? I've ordered the roast chicken but it's going to be a million miles away from a proper roast I'd normally have.' I hoped it wouldn't rub his nose in to the fact he was having soup later, since at least one of us would have something half-decent.

'Ahhhh, I *love* a roast!' Michael came alive again. 'A carvery! I *love* a carvery! Do you love a carvery, Philip?' Michael's passion and excitement was undeniable.

I chuckled at how passionate he was at the sheer idea of a carvery. 'Of course. Who doesn't love a carvery?' I gave him the words he wanted to hear.

Emblazoned with the new connection between us, Michael bounced from foot to foot with pure excitement. 'Hah! Yeah! When we get outta here, Philip, we'll go for a carvery. D'you know the Toby carvery in Langley?' Michael was so thrilled with everything that I would have said I knew it, even if I didn't. One thing I was aware of was that the Langley Toby had become infamous for being inundated with our Travelling Brethren. People just like Michael.

My laughter continued. 'Yeah, I know it. They do a great carvery.'

'Yeah? Yeah! Yes, they do. Yeah. When I get outta here, I'm gonna go to the Toby carvery. You should come too! Yeah! It will be my treat. You and your family. At the Toby carvery. I'll pay for you and the family, Philip.'

Michael meant it. I could tell. A man, that clearly had very little money, that barely knew me, offered to pay for all five of my family to join him and his family for dinner. It was a unique situation. Firstly, I was amazed, stunned, that someone would be so incredibly generous. I felt amused, for want of a better word - Michael was so passionate with his invitation the whole thing was comical. We both smiled. Could someone feel honoured and revolted at the same time? As Michael asked me out, I immediately thought that I couldn't possibly tell Ali that we were all invited out with a bunch of pikeys - to the most pikey-ist of places around. I had to think fast on my feet (even though I was sat in my chair).

'No. Michael. No, mate. You really don't have to do that. My boys are adults, it would cost you an absolute fortune! That is very kind of you, really it is, but there's no way I could get you to pay for my lot.' My response seemed to go down OK, and although Michael had stopped his bounces, he maintained his smile. 'Let's just get ourselves out of here first, and see how we feel, OK?'

'OK. Yeah.' Michael mused. 'I can't wait to get outta 'ere.'

'You'll have to give me your number though – in case my mate lets me down with my roof.' The words came out of my mouth unnecessarily, and I should have let Michael be distracted with delicious dreams of our escape, but instead I clumsily dragged him back to thoughts of our reunion on the outside.

It was horrible to admit, but I had no intention of a meet up with Michael. I was still too prejudiced - still way too much of a massive snob. Ordinarily, I wouldn't have felt so uncomfortable for long, but that man's path had not only crossed mine, but it had entwined and woven together and we had somehow joined forces to help each other fight through our most significant battle. I could look at Michael and see a good man. He loved his family more than anything else, just like me. We had come from totally different places and were different people in so many ways and yet, when it came to important shit, we were identical. I felt terrible that I couldn't embrace his offer – what a wanker I'd become – talk about being killed with kindness.

Before Michael got the chance to double his efforts and convince me to accept his wild offer, we were interrupted by a nurse. She had trolleyed in her blood pressure machine and wanted to check all my obs. I felt so bad about the rejection that I was happy to run away and have a blood pressure machine attempt another haemorrhage on my arm.

'I'll catch you later,' I said to excuse myself from the conversation.

'Yeah. See ya later, Philip.'

23

Visiting Time Again

The timeslots for visits that Michael and I had booked were one after the other. Michael's missus was not on time for their 2pm allocation. Lisa eventually turned up a good fifteen minutes late, flustered. She looked a fair bit younger than Michael - my guess was twenty, but she could have been two years either side of that. She was tiny and yet her jeans seemed at least two sizes bigger than her petite size. She clearly liked to buy clothes from Sports Direct. She probably had stretched out her budget to get as many different coloured Puma T-shirts, Lonsdale hoodies and Umbro sweatshirts as she could. Bleached blonde hair, verging on white, with tied back harshly into a ponytail, her face looked pink although the stress of the journey to the hospital, and the strain from the tight ponytail had possibly made it pinker. I tried not to stare, and we didn't make eye contact, but I couldn't make out if her eyes were light blue because I sensed a redness that surrounded them. I don't think she had cried, but I guessed she naturally had red eyes to match her pink face. No make-up on, she looked knackered. It seemed like the commitment to care for a new baby would do that to anyone.

There was no immediate sign of affection between them. No hugs or kisses. They greeted each other with an 'Alright?', answered with a 'Yeah'. It was funny because they said those two words at the same time. It was also amusing that they didn't think that the conversation start-up was comic – I guessed it was their usual greeting.

Before they got into a conversation, a nurse charged over. Apparently, Lisa had walked into the building, hadn't checked in, had no facemask with her, and the nurse took a serious tone with all the rule breaks. She shot Lisa in the forehead with a red laser beam from her temperature gun and, fortunately for everyone, the gun confirmed a green number. 36.6 degrees was a pass. Lisa took the facemask that was offered, but she didn't apologise. She wasn't being rude deliberately, but she seemed a bit taken aback, oblivious that there were any rules. The nurse left them to it with a parting shot that next time, Lisa had to check in at the desk, or she wouldn't be welcome through.

As she donned the light-blue mask, Lisa pointed up at the whiteboard above Michael's bed and announced, 'They spelt yer name wrong.' Her voice was as quiet as it was common. 'That's not 'ow yer spell Hearn.'

Michael craned his neck around to see where she pointed. 'Yeah.' He agreed. His grin was tinged with embarrassment. 'I told 'em 'ow to spell it though, innit?'

Lisa muttered *tch* as though it was a sound she made a thousand times a day living with poor old Michael. There was both a black marker pen and a cloth attached to the board and Lisa took them, reached up, wiped out their name that had been there for three days and re-wrote their family name, and added the A that had been missed. I could tell that Lisa was the brains of the bunch.

I did my best not to be too nosey, but it was bloody hard not to be when I was such a people-watcher, a piss-taker and generally a nosey bastard. Lisa explained how she got a taxi but it had been an ordeal – something to do with her Uber account – which was why she was late. Yes, the baby was fine. They discussed how Michael was and he tried to explain what the doctors had told him, the main emphasis of which was that they had told him to stop smoking and drinking.

Mobile phones in hospitals had always been a bit of a no-no. I had been very self-conscious about using one at all. It was OK to silently browse the internet, watch football (sound down of course) and to ping out the odd text or message were all perfectly acceptable because all that business was very quiet and wouldn't disturb fellow patients or annoy the staff. But if someone wanted to talk on the phone, no, I wasn't comfortable about that, which was why I hadn't made any calls (alright, maybe a couple of two-minute calls) and had generally stuck to WhatsApp as my chosen route of communication. Michael didn't even have a phone and other than Hecky's dad, nobody in Ward 4 had disturbed the peace with their personal calls. That was until Lisa handed over a phone to Michael at the start of her visit. At first, the transaction might have been just like a burner phone smuggled into HMP Brixton, hidden away and only to be used sparingly for discrete messages for fear of confiscation.

I was so wrong.

Within thirty seconds of being handed the phone, Michael had managed to fire up a video call with his entire family that had been gathered, lying in wait, for that precise moment. As soon as they answered the call there was a loud cacophony of shouts, cheers, whistles, and whoops mixed up with loud and colourful swearing. Like it or not, just by the sheer volume, I couldn't escape the event and was in attendance as a secret bystander. Nobody knew I listened in and even if they did, they didn't care.

The shouts from several different rough voices continued for at least fifteen minutes. I had to admire the way they kept up their intensity for such a long period. Just when the sound and enthusiasm dipped, a new voice entered the scene and another big wave of jeers and yells began. Michael stared at the new phone for most of time, with his fixated grin, and his series of nods, and I heard him say, 'Yeah' every ten seconds. He loved the attention and the gang of gypsies on the other end did their utmost to make Michael feel loved and special, and I was certain that Michael wished he was back home among his brotherhood. I wasn't annoyed because most of their private jokes were funny, and the whole show put a smile on my face. Had my abject snobbery shown signs of weakness?

If the first half of the rowdy video call was full of *hellos* from everyone and whatever else their individual greetings were, then the second half was taken up with all the many *goodbyes* exchanged by everyone at least eight or nine times each – there seemed to be hardly anything in the middle. The farewells were just as joyous and raucous as the greetings and the guestlist that came and went on the call seemed to work back in reverse order to where Michael had started. Eventually, after wave after wave of jeers, they touched the red button to end the call and Lisa and Michael bickered about something or other for several minutes. When their row faded, they shuffled off for a romantic fag. Bless them. They didn't seem to have much between them other than babies, cigarettes and a taste for Sports Direct leisurewear.

The message I longed for came through from Ali. It was a minute before four o'clock and the whole gang waited in the car park, exactly as our masterplan. I had finished soaking up a bag of antibiotics so with no drips plugged into me, I was free to leave Bay 4.

I left my bed in my civvies but, anyone could tell I was no civilian. With the cannula strapped to my hand and with three cotton swabs taped to my lower arms I was obviously an inmate and not a visitor. I hadn't made the trip to the fresh air outside since Luigi had wheeled me on to floor two, to experience that dreadful sound on the previous Friday night. I found the lift, jabbed the button labelled G whilst being disgusted that hundreds of ill, infected people had touched the same button since it was last cleaned. If it ever had been cleaned, I wondered. The door closed and I was safely encapsulated from the evils of the world (apart from a billion deadly germs to keep me company), and the machinery clanked into action and took the metal box, and me, down to the ground floor.

When the door slid away as I landed on the ground floor, I stepped out and headed for the automatic front door - the final barrier. I watched it draw back slowly to reveal my exit. I was out. No guards saw me, let alone stop me.

Ali had left the car and I stood a few yards from the entrance. We didn't say anything; we just smashed together into a hug that said everything we needed to say. The embrace told each other that we were there to support each other, the squeeze confirmed physical strength and determined resolve and the shared contact of our faces spoke of unbreakable, unconditional love.

Everything was positive. There wasn't as much as a flicker of fear between us. I had felt stronger than I'd ever been since my admission, in every sense. It was vitally important for me to show Ali and the kids that I was well, strong, positive and that I had been looked after.

'I won't kiss you on the lips,' Ali said as I released her from my grip. 'You know, just in case. I'm paranoid we'll give you something.'

Ali was petrified that she might pass on Covid or anything nasty for that matter. She had made the whole troop take a lateral flow test. As far as I was concerned, it was far more likely that I'd infect them with something evil from the hospital, so I accepted the kiss ban even though I craved the intimacy.

'OK, Ali. We'll make up for it when I finally get sent home from here.' I smiled and we were both convinced that a discharge had to be soon. It *had* to be.

Ali escorted me over to where she had parked and all three of our kids poked their heads out of the car windows with great big smiles on their faces. As soon as I was close, they jumped out to give me a whole bunch of hugs. These happened in reverse age order. Lydia bounded over first, and the boys waited patiently until she had finished her grip of me. Lydia gave me a mock sad face and told me that she wanted me home because she missed me so much. She fished out my white gold chain from beneath her T-shirt to show she had kept it safe around her neck and slept in my bed and wore my white Muhammad Ali T-shirt every night (for the smell apparently). She said she wanted me back home. I reassured her that I had done (and would do) everything I could, to get back to her as quickly as I possibly could.

I didn't normally get the chance to hug my sons. They'd aged into 20-year-old men and they still lived with me. I couldn't remember the last time I hugged either of them. It had been a long time, but we had the perfect excuse to end that drought. They'd never know how grateful I was for both of those man-to-man embraces. I got to cuddle my wife and my daughter a lot. It was dead easy to be affectionate with the girls, so when I held Jayden and then Harrison, it genuinely meant the world to me. Of course, there were no sentimental words to accompany the act of affection. Both boys were up to date with all the medical news (still many tests before any conclusions) so any verbal expressions of love from me during these physical exchanges might get them suspicious that maybe something was up - maybe I did know that I faced a death sentence? Lydia still hadn't been told anything serious, only that I had undergone several tests – and had a few more to endure – but I now felt better from all the sickness stuff. I was satisfied that everyone held their shit together and we teamed up as a powerful and strong unit. Either that, or those four had secretly been to acting lessons.

The hour we spent was joyous, full of smiles and laughs. We spoke about how awful Wales had been in the Euros to distract us from why we were in a hospital car park, and we were all in good spirits considering the cloud of doom that swelled above us. They kindly didn't mention that they were going home to enjoy a tasty roast dinner. Everyone was just like Fonzie; everyone was cool. Kool and the Gang. The tension was there for me, but the importance of keeping the mood light and fluffy was more powerful and therefore it defeated any negativity that festered beneath the surface. We did not discuss the herd of elephants in the car park.

Before we knew it, we were back to big hugs and we said our goodbyes. I told each one of my children to look after their mum, asked them to help around the house and they all confirmed that they would behave, and Lydia said she'd stay in her mum's bed as their mutual comfort helped them to sleep. Time had beaten me once again. Reluctantly, I returned to the entrance door. I turned around as I got there, and they all waved from the car.

Don't worry guys, I thought, *I'll get this battle done and get back to you, and beautiful boring normality, soon.*

I had to wait for someone through the glass to buzz me back into the building and then I managed to find my route back to Bay 4 easily. I climbed on to my bed, content with the knowledge that I had four massive reasons to conquer all the pancreatic tumour business. Those gorgeous people had recharged me, and the remainder of my sentence should be piss-easy from there on. England were down to play Germany on Tuesday. I had told them that I would be home to watch the match with them in two days. That was a guarantee.

With the caveat that my fucking body had to behave itself.

Sunday Roast

The doctors had completed their shifts and the visits from friends and family were over. We headed into the home straight of Sunday with the announcement of Sunday dinner. I heard the bell toll twice. I was hungry, which had to be a good sign, and I wondered what their mass-produced roast dinner was going to look like.

I put my book down, got down from the bed and made myself comfortable in my chair in pure anticipation. The catering lady came to me last. I would've served me last as well. She started with bed number 1 and worked her way over to me in bed 4, a logical order that even a hungry man could respect.

The meal was edible.

For a starter, to spark up my digestive juices, I ate half the tough bread roll that I pasted with some cold Country Life butter. The butter must have thawed during the day as I could actually cut a bit off the edge and apply it to the roll. It tasted acceptable, the butter helped, but I didn't want to let the main course get any colder than I suspected it would be, so I parked the roll back on the small plate and went for the chicken. I detected a modest-sized breast with a splatter of gravy, two small roast potatoes, a spoonful of sliced carrots and a tough, mini-sized Yorkshire pudding which was there to remind us that it really was a Sunday roast. I imagined I was on board an aeroplane because the meal reminded me of the typical ones I'd had on flights – kid-sized and with a hidden musk of a dinner that had been reheated, except the meal that sat in front of me hadn't been surrounded by the fun of a holiday.

The chicken was acceptable, but I couldn't get more excited than that. I suspected it was probably the best meal they offered on the menu. Chicken was chicken – which wasn't a particularly profound statement – but it was edible and at least it wasn't pink.

I'd admit that I have a sweet tooth, like my mother, so if I ever had got a millimetre of room in my stomach, I'd squeeze down a pudding of some description. I'd always listed a summer fruit crumble as my chosen death row, last meal dessert. It had tempted me from the menu, the picture looked delicious, so I couldn't resist. It was fair to say that I'd never had a crumble like that one before. I deduced that it had been made by a satanist. There was a teaspoon of blackberry jam (I hoped it was jam) hidden by a big handful of Rich Tea biscuit dust. It was one hell of a challenge to eat the half that I did. The average person would not have been able to summon up the incredible amount of saliva needed to finish off the so called 'dessert'. The biscuit dust was so dry and bland, I wondered if I'd accidentally ordered a *desert*.

Fortunately, I had a cup of water on my tray, so I flushed down anything that was stuck in my mouth and throat. Anyone that watched me might have seen me slowly shake my head in disbelief at how that meal had ended. The main thing was that I'd survived it, another event ticked off as I strived towards my release day. Maybe tomorrow would be my final couple of meals before I had the freedom to make something from my own kitchen.

I watched all the football on my phone, since it was the best way to grind out what was left of the weekend. The hospital Wi-Fi was so erratic it was painful and I had to watch more of the little blue buffering circle than any decent matches. I didn't bother to look for a TV room; no doubt Covid protocols were still in place to kill any communal fun. For the record, I remembered that Eden Hazard's seemingly ordinary brother scored a goal for Belgium and knocked out Portugal. Soon after, the Dutch managed to be awful enough to lose to the Czech Republic, 2-0. It helped get me to bedtime, but it also made me long to be at home, with the boys. We could have been there as we picked the teams apart with our constant (and slightly mean) piss-taking.

I had got used to the last acts of each day; my routine had become familiar to me – I wasn't happy about it – and it made me feel a little institutionalised. I padded over to the bathroom, had a final wee and brushed my teeth. The weekend was done, and Monday was getting itself ready for me and the rest of the world. I hated to have time off work, but what could I do when I had been imprisoned in hospital? The call to work-colleague Tony on Saturday was a good move. He understood because he was still in recovery after his prostate had been removed. There were going to be some important decisions to sort out at work and I was already a day behind because of all the illness-business that had started on Friday. As I brushed my teeth, I knew that all that work shit would simply have to bloody wait – just like Pelé, and everything else.

I returned to my bed and exchanged messages with Ali. I laid down my plan to steam through whatever tests where needed on Monday, so they had no excuse to keep me in any longer than necessary. As much as Ali wanted me home, she also wanted me to be thoroughly cared for and completely tested to the nth degree, so we knew the journey ahead and if that meant I needed to spend a month in hospital, then so be it. The chat with Ali had calmed me down, but she would be up for several more hours so she could play out even more permutations in her mind, whilst I fell to sleep quickly.

Monday, Monday

Bouncy and buoyant. That was my mood when I woke up on Monday morning. Although I was still on the course of antibiotics, and therefore getting plumbed into my cannula every few hours, I had been otherwise freed from the constant IV drip. Freedom had been granted because I could take in food and water in the usual way. It meant that for most of the night, I had been able to sleep in a more familiar position without the worry that I might tug on my tubes or crush them or pull the bloody things out. A much better night's sleep and the target of full recovery was now in sight.

Let's get this day done and dusted. It had become my new mantra. I attacked Monday as if it was a day of work. I had already been stirred early by the nurse and her observations. The permanent connection to the drip was over, but the obs – well, they just kept on and on. Blood pressure and everything else for the hundredth time, but I deliberately didn't go back to sleep. To make sure I didn't drift back to sleep I scrolled through utter rubbish on my phone (yes, even my dodgy phone was fully charged). It did kick start my brain into gear and it dragged me on to 6am, which was an acceptable time to rise and shine. Based on my now extensive experience, I knew that the breakfast dude threatened to wheel in his *cart of disappointment* at any time from 6:45 to 7:30am so, whilst everything was calm, I threw on some clothes so I could make a beeline for the bathroom.

The bathroom was designed as a wet room, with a shower head fixed to the wall at the far end, a drain gulley nearby it, housed within the vinyl flooring, rather than there being a separate cubicle or shower tray. Because I intended to treat the day like any normal workday, I started my routine off with a morning wee and an invigorating shower, just as I normally would. There was a white plastic chair directly under the shower head that was clearly there for those requiring a sit-down shower. I had brought in a whole armful of wash things and clothes but, in the absence of any hooks or shelving, the chair was ideal to keep my towel, clothes and washbag off the floor. After relieving myself with a dark orange wee (which, I believed, sounded more optimistic than the description of light brown), I moved the garden chair out of the way of the shower, stripped off, and I tucked my socks into my shoes and then used the chair to balance all my clothes (T-shirt, trackie bottoms, and pants). That chair had evolved into a full-sized hospital version of Buck-A-Roo. I made sure the old clothes were on the bottom of the pile, fresh clothes above, topped off with the towel Ali had given me from home – but if any of my things were to hit the highly toxic floor – it would mean an instant *Game Over*.

The shower was not heavenly as such, I wouldn't want to exaggerate, but I'd give it an above satisfactory 7 out of 10. Once I'd worked out how to get the water warm enough to hammer down my goosebumps and at a force more powerful than the default of *light drizzle*, I was able to scrub off the sweat, grime and God knows what else, that had accumulated on me since Friday morning. I shampooed my hair twice. I used up a third of the shower gel in and around my groin, my arse and my armpits and I even used conditioner in my hair. The mishmash of products made me smell like a raw coconut that had been dipped in vanilla ice cream with a hint of jasmine (assuming jasmine smelled flowery). I had to be extremely careful not to get the plaster on my right arm wet, as it held my cannula in place. That proved to be impossible, and it got wet. I knew the effectiveness of the adhesive had been breached – it started to flap. Bloody cannulas!

I removed a lot of the adhesive from the dozens of plasters and tabs I'd been peppered with since arrival. The black gum from the ECG pads proved to be the hardest challenge of all. I scrubbed my body vigorously and the majority of the pads were replaced by red blotches all over my chest as a temporary reminder to what I'd endured over the weekend. I couldn't get all the black gunk off in that first shower.

Disappointed, I resigned myself to a new plan – anything that I failed to scrape off, I could remove in the comfort of my own shower, back home. Or, maybe, in the bloody shower tomorrow morning, if my plan to escape from Colditz later that day failed miserably.

I took my time to complete the rest of my routine. I normally sported a fair amount of stubble on my face, but it had been a few days since I'd bothered with my appearance so I was now well into the realms of beardy. I took out my trusty beard-trimmer and made a half-decent attempt to hack my whiskers down to the equivalent of a couple of days' worth of stubble. All the while, I was bent down to look into the tiny mirror that was so steamed up I couldn't see what I did. The mirror had obviously been installed by someone well under 6 feet tall because my back started to twinge as I continued my battle to attack the stray hairs on my chin that I just couldn't seem to locate. I felt old, and I had to straighten up and bend backwards to ease my back. My back was not happy – I needed to bend over again in a final attempt to get those last few bristles.

Once I'd had enough of that palaver, I squeezed out some shaving gel and lathered up my cheeks that were still soft and warm from the shower. In front of the miniscule mirror, I attempted a wet shave with a middle-aged Gillette razor. For some time, I'd only shaved my cheeks rather than the tougher whiskers around my jawline, so that bad boy of a razor with its five blades had seemed to be immortal. Shame I couldn't see my artistry - my reflection was still a misty blur.

A shit, a shower and a shave. Without the shit, unfortunately. The lack of bowel movement niggled me. Rupert, one of the guys from my poker group, had sent me several messages but most of them were, 'Have you had a poo yet?' He seemed worried that they wouldn't let me go unless I gave birth to a healthy baby turd. Rupert had experience of bowel operations and I realised that I had gained new respect for people that I knew where I hadn't appreciated what they'd gone through in the past. The hospital experience gave me a new level of understanding, respect, and compassion. I didn't even bother to strain one out at first light. My plan was to order something spicy on the menu – that sometimes worked for expectant mothers, so why not me?

I thought those thoughts whilst I brushed my teeth (I did not swallow the tap water as it most certainly was contaminated with parasites that ate the brain) and then I managed to wipe a section of the mirror clear so I could poke some contact lenses on to my eyeballs. I ditched my glasses, and it did make me feel more like my normal self. An extra-long spray of deodorant under each armpit and a carefully choreographed dance to put on some fresh clothes (without dropping anything on that septic floor) concluded the procedure. I bundled up the old clothes, my towel and my washbag and walked out of the bathroom as new man. I was no longer a patient, albeit in my own eyes. I just needed the doctors to realise I was as right as rain, so they could send me on my merry way.

If I could just do a poo, I thought, then they couldn't deny me freedom.

I went back to my bed, and I saw that Michael continued to snooze as I passed him. I sat in my chair and read Richard Osman's book to kill some time – until l I heard the breakfast bell ring out.

When breakfast came, I ordered two bits of Weetabix, although it might have been an own-brand equivalent. The milk thought about being a temperature just below that of the water that had been sat next to me throughout the night, it was almost cold. I did ask for sugar. I had diabetes, but I think I'd rather have gone into a hyperglycaemic coma than eat Tesco's version of Weetabix neat. It went down OK, I was hungry and got the cereal inside me before it reached that point when Weetabix gave up on life and disintegrated into a milky, bitty gazpacho.

I chanced the toast again. What can I say, the lure of the individual marmalade drew me in once more. I didn't bother to cut it into triangles, and instead a full-sized, orange-tasting rectangle was good enough that morning. Once I'd finished the toast, I popped out a solitary Metformin pill from the strip and swallowed it dry so it could land on top of all that food in my stomach, and silently perform whatever magic it was destined to accomplish.

The tea, to flush all the food and medicine down, was pretty good.

I was surprised, as a complete tea snob, at how good the tea was compared to everything else. I made the mental note that hospital tea started off *good* first thing each morning, but that was it, from then on it deteriorated at an alarming rate to *undrinkable* by lunchtime, and by evening I would rate it as *hazardous to health*.

A different catering person came by to clear away everything from my tray. I'd eaten it all like a good boy and expressed my gratitude. I had every intention to be the perfect patient all day long. Gold stars all the way. Without doubt, if they let anyone out early for good behaviour, it would be me.

There was a morning handover going on and although I couldn't fully make out their conversation, I heard them say my name after I sensed the gathering of staff. I knew there was going to be new batch of doctors and nurses, as I'd heard them speak about me in the corridor before they walked over to me.

As predicted, a completely new team of doctors introduced themselves at the foot of my bed. Dr Nikolaidis lead his band of four. He looked smart and gave me the impression of intelligence because he had some nice spectacles on. Dr Nikolaidis told me that they had read my notes and asked if he could examine me. I dutifully obliged and lifted up my T-shirt to expose my belly. The assessment was a general feel around my tummy with the simultaneous questions such as – did I feel any pain – as he pressed into me at various locations. I confirmed that there was no pain, other than I felt the pressure from his fingers as I normally would expect. He was serious but I sensed he might be more chatty and friendly than the weekend guy, D'Freitas.

Nikolaidis gave it to me straight. The results from the blood they sucked out of me yesterday was encouraging and they were satisfied that I had beaten back my unspecified infection. However, today was going to be one of more tests.

'We want you to have another chest X-ray and another scan. We also need to check for certain trackers and indicators in your blood, so there will be more blood tests I'm afraid.'

'That's OK with me,' I said, in the guise of the model patient that had reached the point of not giving a fuck about how many more needles they could possibly stick in me.

'Good, good,' said the Doctor. 'Sam here...' he pointed out a tall doctor that had rolled up sleeves, just like himself, '...is a junior doctor

– is it alright with you, if he examines you?'

I reckon they knew they could get away with anything with me. I was so desperate to co-operate they'd have half a chance with gross malpractice. What could I say?

'That is fine with me,' I replied with a positive smile towards Sam.

Nikolaidis thanked me, then held out his gloved hand, palm up, towards me and looked over at Sam. His gesture appeared that I had been offered out as the main prize to the young apprentice.

After a polite pause, Sam dived straight in. He mimicked the entire examination that his senior had carried out. *Well done*, I thought, *at least you paid attention*. We went through the charade where Sam asked me whether I was in any pain, which I confirmed that I still wasn't. Sam even took my pulse for good measure. He thanked me and I told him he was very welcome. I wondered if he had manged to feel anything noticeably different as he pushed into my medically interesting pancreas and, more importantly, its impressive neuroendocrine tumour. I didn't ask.

With the potentially private matters concluded, they pulled back the curtains. Dr Nikolaidis pointed out another Doctor, on the far side of our bay that stood over at the bed occupied by Hecky's dad with the record-breaking bollocks.

'That is Dr Hasim. He is one of our urologists and he has agreed to come and see you later today, to check on your prostate.'

'Oh alright, thank you,' I said as Dr Nikolaidis and the team left to continue their rounds.

Then, just when I thought they'd left, Dr Nikolaidis doubled-back and flipped over the pages on his clipboard, presumably because he had seen something on my notes that he needed clarity on. He pointed at the first page and looked back at me and said, 'I'm sorry, but it says on here that you're fifty. Is that correct?' His question was laced with surprise.

That was a relief, because for a moment I thought he was about to say something serious.

'Yes,' I confirmed, with a smile of respite and a little pride.

'Wow!' he said, 'I would have said you were much younger than me. I'm forty-four!'

I too, would have said he was older than me. I was lucky enough to have inherited genes to keep my hair intact, with only a few flecks of grey. Dr Nikolaidis was practically bald, with a nicely tanned head lined with the odd streak of combed back, dark hair. There was enough grey around the sides of his head to suggest he was living in the second half of his life. Maybe his glasses and smart attire compared to my casual look and no glasses betrayed our real age difference. Maybe because I felt so much better, I might have been one of the most energised patients he'd see that week.

'Well, I do my best to avoid stress,' I joked. 'If I'd been doing your job for the last thirty years, I'm sure my hair would be white by now.'

'Ha-ha,' the doctor laughed. 'Maybe, maybe. But you do look well, and you are young, and you are fit so that will all help in your recovery.'

I thanked him and after I disagreed about me being fit, we exchanged goodbyes and he left to catch up with his team.

Recovery? I considered this. I did feel as well as I could be, and my mood was positive. I was in no pain, and I felt good both physically and mentally. Yes, I thought, I was strong enough to battle through whatever treatment they threw at me, all guns blazing. *Recovery*, from whatever my cancer shit turned out to be, WAS an option.

Time

Time for my prostate examination.

No time like the present for something so enjoyable.

Dr Hasim arrived at my quarters. I recognised him from when Dr Nikolaidis pointed him out earlier. Physically he looked like a combination between Indiana Jones' fez-wearing friend Salleh and the big Turkish prison boss in Midnight Express. From afar, I had seen him in action, and he didn't take any shit.

Earlier, after my new specialist team had left me to digest their update, I had watched Dr Hasim and, more importantly, heard him speak to Hecky's dad. Their discussion got heated. Chris had said that there was no way he could go home because his balls were still so big and sensitive that, for him to be out and at home, well, it would not be possible. It was not possible because he had tried to stay home twice before and further complications to his condition had resulted in him being readmitted straight back to A&E. To compound this, Chris said, he had an exceptionally enthusiastic two-year old that lay in wait for him at home. There was no way he could keep his son (the wonderfully delightful Hecky) down. He would jump all over his dad. Chris seemed adamant that his only safe place, away from pain, was in the hospital, and he couldn't possibly go home.

Dr Hasim listened – but was not impressed – he had none of it.

He told Chris that there was nothing else they could do for him. They were satisfied that the infection was under control, and they were equally satisfied that the swelling had improved well enough for them to discharge him. Chris was told that he was in the surgery ward and there were other patients that needed the bed. Dr Hasim told his patient that he needed to sort his situation back home because they planned to complete all their paperwork and he would be forced to leave. There wasn't much Chris could say in response and Dr Hasim politely said goodbye and left the ward.

I wondered if Chris' discharge was fully under control in both meanings of the word.

That time had come though. Dr Hasim had come back, and he stood by my bed.

He introduced himself, and he seemed perfectly friendly. He said that he had discussed my case with Dr Nikolaidis and, if I was OK with it, he was here to carry out a prostate examination to see if there were any irregularities that might cause him concern. I said that I was fine with it. When asked I confirmed that yes, I had undergone the procedure before. The doctor stated that he had done his job for over twenty years and he would soon tell me if there was anything for me to worry about. Or not.

He pulled the curtains closed and suddenly it was just he and I. Under the doctor's instruction, I rolled over on to my left-hand side and faced the wall away from him. I pulled down my trackie bottoms down to my knees. My underwear followed straight after. My whole arse was now exposed. The doctor told me to bring my knees up to my chest and I obliged. I stared at the wall and thought, *here we go*.

Whilst I had prepared myself, Dr Hasim had donned some latex gloves. He also ripped open two sachets of Optilube. The chosen lubricant brand of Wexham Park urologists, or so it seemed. KY was so cliché.

I suddenly had a thought spring out and I called out a warning to the doctor, 'Sorry, I haven't had a poo for a few days so I'm not sure what you'll find there and if that, erm, is going to cause a problem?'

'That shouldn't be an issue. In fact, this might help you to go after, if that has been a concern,' the beefy doctor confirmed. 'Now. Please. Try to relax.'

Those words sent a chill right through me and before I knew it, his finger penetrated my anus. I had failed to take his advice – I was not relaxed. The sphincter muscle of my arsehole seemed to have a mind of its own and fluctuated between tense and relaxed. I struggled to find any calmness at such a delicate, intimate place, and my natural urge was to tense-up and prevent any sort of foreign invasion. The internal battle of tension happened three feet away from my brain and I tried my best to keep my arsehole in a state half-way between shut tight (as a duck's arse) and gaped, porno-style.

Another man was inside me. My defences had been well and truly breached.

He was a big man, with unforgiving sized digits. Two! I realised. He'd forced TWO fucking big fingers inside me! I prayed to whichever God that was the one that represented fingered patients. *Get this over with quickly.*

I drew upon the inspiration of my wife. Three times she had given birth. Three times she had gone through the most frightening, most painful experience that I could only attempt to imagine. Yes, I had been there, but I was a million miles away from the pain. A side plot to the endurance of pregnancy and the act of labour was the sheer loss of privacy and dignity. As I lay there with Christ knows how many knuckles from a stranger inside me, I thought that it was only a mere fraction of the many things Ali, and billions of other women, had experienced. My dignity left the building days ago when that young doctor had fondled my genitals in front of me, but the prostate episode had been the pinnacle and I consoled myself with the thought that from that point on, everything else had to be downhill, a breeze, and I just needed to lay back (on my side) and mentally find a happy place.

I felt Dr Hasim's fingers move about. I wondered how the doctors even hunted down a prostate. Surely, it was just a mass of soft flesh inside there. He talked as he slowly assessed my inner-most private gland. He spoke good English with his appealing (Moorish and moreish) accent, which was thick with bass, and his tone sounded calm, confident, and I was sure it soothed many of his patients. He probably did it to distract me, so that I couldn't focus 100% on what happened inside my bottom.

It helped; my thoughts were split.

1% on our verbal intercourse and, quick maths, 99% on our digital intercourse.

'I can tell that your prostate is indeed enlarged. It is larger than what I would expect from a man of your age.'

Dr Hasim's instant prognosis was not a surprise to me. I kept silent though as I didn't want to accidentally speak out the words I thought, *Can you please remove your hand now?*

The doctor carried on, and he worked diligently inside me. The lubricant did a fantastic job and kept any real pain at arm's length, but the sensation was uncomfortable to say the least – both physically and emotionally. Surely, the expert had gathered all the information he could possibly need within the first 5 seconds of meeting my prostate. Did he need a full topographical survey and a condition report of every nook and cranny so he could rebuild a larger-than life clay model in his office?

'The good news is that it feels smooth and quite regular,' he continued with his verbal report.

I was happy to receive any good news whilst stuck in my unbearably awkward situation.

'Yes, you see I would be concerned if I could feel any bumps or if the surface of the gland was rough,' he said.

I remained stoic and silent but thought, *Thanks, for that doc, are we quite done now?*

It felt like I'd been *on the hook* for several minutes but I had lost track of time altogether as the invasion started to edge towards the realms of eternity.

From somewhere behind me, I heard Dr Hasim's voice. 'After I've finished, I will give you a cup for you to do a urine sample straight after. Now, I'm going to put something into your bladder, and this should be something we can pick up in the sample, OK?'

What the fuck?

I had a split second to either object or comply and because I was on my best behaviour, I just accepted the situation. I was like putty in the doctor's hands. I did not respond with, *'What EXACTLY are you putting in my bladder?'* and *'How are you going to do that with your sausage fingers?'*

What I did say, rather meekly, was, 'OK.'

I felt his fingers move again. There must have been some sort of prostate stroke going on, albeit only a couple of seconds worth. Something muscular contracted inside me at the focal point of that new action. It wasn't a big spasm, more a subtle twinge. I'd like to think I was a man of the world, but for just those few seconds I desperately wanted to be blessed with ignorance. Some men were really into having their prostate *massaged*. It wasn't something I'd ever desired or engaged in. It wasn't a turn on, but I will at least acknowledge that some guys loved it. Each to their own.

I believe he gave me some weird semi-orgasm. There was no identifiable ejaculation to speak of, just an uncomfortable spasm just behind where I'd normally expect to feel *the real thing*. Something had happened but I ignored it or chose to think that maybe I was being paranoid or (please God) wrong. I let the violation go without any further discussion – it helped me block it out from my memories. Completely blanked out; until I would decide to write about it.

Come to think of it, Dr Hasim did also look a lot like Harvey Weinstein.

Within seconds of my rather unexpected climax, the ordeal was over. Dr Hasim carefully withdrew his fingers from my anus and quickly grabbed at a wad of paper towels.

'All done,' he announced. He sounded proud of us both.

I may as well tell you that I reckoned his fingers were coated in my shit. Fortunately, for all of us, he still wore the latex gloves and I witnessed Dr Hasim do an expert manoeuvre with the paper towels as he wiped his fingers and gripped hard enough so that he could pull the glove off his nicely warmed up right hand. He walked through the gap in the privacy curtain and took the bundle of dirty paper and latex over to the bin by the window. He stamped on the foot pedal and the lid sprang open to receive the offensive waste. The lid slammed shut as the bundle (the evidence?) entered the bin's jaws. Next journey, the incinerator.

The doctor began his summary. 'I'm sure you are alright. If you were not, you would have been kicking and screaming.'

I bloody well was on the inside, I thought.

'Here you go.' Dr Hasim had offered me my own wad of paper towels. 'Well done.'

'Thanks,' I muttered and, like his virgin bride, I accepted the towels and used them to clean my messy crack. With his deep-space exploration done, the doctor left the scene.

My silent little prayer had been answered, as there wasn't any sign of blood. There was a lot of sticky lubricant to mop up, and I used all the towels. I saw only a token amount of faeces on the wipes, which was a bonus. I didn't know where to put my bundle of used paper towels, so I stuffed the wad into the cardboard puke bowl that had been redundant on my bed-tray since I'd stopped throwing up two days before. The bowl and the evidence of my examination was about to end up in the same medical waste bin but, first, I had to pull up my knickers and my trousers.

Once I'd made myself decent, I slid off the bed, dumped the card bowl and its contents into the pedal bin and moped off to the toilet, accompanied with the white plastic cup I'd been handed. I wasn't bursting but did manage to muster up enough urine to fill half the cup. Water was one thing, but when it came to a cup of piss, I think that the optimists would say that it was half empty. I wondered what small percentage of the amber liquid had been semen, rather than urine. I placed the cup on the floor (there were no cisterns on show; everything was hidden) and sat on the toilet to attempt a bowel movement. If there was going to be a silver lining to the whole episode it would be the pleasure of experiencing my own version of the Dambusters now that the gates had been devastated. Had my intestines been encouraged and agitated enough to clear out four days' worth of shit?

No.

I allowed gravity an attempt at it, but even that couldn't force the issue. My bum was certainly not in the market for a full prolapse situation, so I gave up after a few minutes.

When I left the bathroom, I stood by the nurses' desk for a few minutes and waited for someone to collect my sample. I couldn't just leave it there on the desk, because a) it would be unhygienic, b) some cleaner might clear it away, or worse case, c) some minesweeper might think it is a warm Liebfraumilch and take a cheeky gulp. Anything was possible in that bloody place.

Eventually, I spotted a nurse, and I insisted she take half a cup of warm piss from me. I explained it was my sample for the urology doctor. She politely thanked me and, quite literally, took the piss. I headed off in the opposite direction, back to the shelter of my bed. My mood, like my bottom, had been damaged.

I sought out some solace from my closest friends. I sent out a message in the group chat, since they hadn't heard from me in a while. I told them that my examination felt like the doctor had tried to fish out the last slippery olive out of the bottom of a tall jar. Their responses achieved their goal – they made me smile.

Richard: Are you sure it wasn't Panda?
Sounds like the sort of thing he'd be doing.

GaryMan: You've been milked. Like a cow.

Sean: Fucking Hell Phil – are you sure it was a genuine doctor? It sounds like he used you like a bowling ball.

Panda: I wish it was me.

Phil: Cheers guys

I needed a few minutes in solitude. To laugh off that whole/hole ordeal had been one way to cope, but I also had to take a breath in my own space and regain my composure. I made a vow to myself that I would escape from all the crap very, very soon. I curled up on my bed, pulled the thin white sheet over me and allowed myself five minutes to feel sorry for myself.

Rebel Alliance

There was to be no planned visit from Ali. As much as I would've loved the distraction, I was fine with the plan. She wouldn't normally come and visit me at work on a Monday and I wanted to remain in a focussed, work-like mode to bully-on through the day.

Ali had recovered from the shock from my call on Saturday - the tears had flowed several miles away from me and she proved just how strong and supportive she was. Actually, we both proved it to each other. I showed her I was in good shape, and that gave rise to enough faith that all would be alright and that a state of panic or manic worrying was not going to help or change the situation. Ali needed a break from the intensity of the weekend freak out. We agreed that she should at least try to go to work and get some normality back, to prove to the rest of the family that there was no need to panic and, as I said over and over, I would be home soon.

The kids also had a perfectly normal, boring Monday. Harrison was out at Pinewood Studios all day, editing showreels for aspiring actors, Lydia went to school and Jayden was left at home to enjoy his last few days of his final summer holiday before his Siemens apprenticeship started – which probably meant an all-day binge-fest of FIFA or Call of Duty or whatever game was on his PlayStation. Rather than a visit, Ali and I decided on a planned phone call, once she was back from work, at around 4:00pm.

It helped me to know that they were all otherwise occupied and not making themselves sick with worry. I wasn't worried but I felt unsure and unsettled, and uncertain about what was in store for me. I did a great job to just block out as much as I could. I refused to think about anything I didn't know about and adopted a method of being focussed on each baby step, each little test (or big-fingered test), and every scan or blood test. My philosophy had worked so far, so I kept on with my method to take each thirty-minute chunk of each day as they came, all in my stride.

As planned, I made a call to the private healthcare company that I had been signed up to. I had my paperwork and after I hung on for a good ten minutes (who said private was better?), I finally spoke to a human. It became an unsuccessful call very quickly. An efficiently polite woman wanted to know what was wrong with me and what specialist I needed. I said that it was early days, and I didn't know any of that important stuff. I was told to investigate and then get back to her, whereupon she could help. As I ended the call, I realised that by the time I knew the story, I would probably be out of hospital. I immediately gave up any dreams of a comfortable, private room and resigned myself to a further night next to Michael and further meals from Wexham Park's notorious à la carte menu.

It was quiet in our ward. Raj was asleep and Michael was up and about, no doubt to get some fresh air (sucked through a cigarette filter). I made the effort to have my 'Dad Chat' with Chris Balls (which was the new full name I had given him), and I ventured over to the far side of bay 4.

The plan for the conversation was:

- Offer some sympathy with regards to his testicle-related problems.
- Suggest he employed a proper lawyer; he should seek some compensation from the private surgery that had caused such a catastrophic catalogue of events.
- Suggest he stayed at his parent's house (or anyone else's), if he genuinely could not be at home with the notorious Hecky. Anything had to be better than hospital.

I'd say it mostly went as planned. Obviously, I introduced myself and as he lay there (after he had removed his headphones and put aside his iPad), and I confessed that I had overheard about the disaster he'd been through. Chris Balls was happy to divulge his story to me. It was horrific. I'll let him release his own story in his own time. The headlines were bad enough – sometimes our imagination could dream up even worse situations than the truth. Everyone in earshot knew that the saga of Chris's infected bollocks had dragged on for six weeks. I started to get the impression that he had retold his tale of torment several times already. When I suggested the employment of a proper lawyer he politely nodded and let me blather on about how he should scrap for every penny of compensation and he was not to get a *no win – no fee* cheap version. He stayed quiet as I banged on about doing some homework, check out reviews and engage with a fully recommended bastard that knew every angle and loophole as it would all be worth it in the long run.

At the end of my battle-cry, there was a pause between us, and then the penny dropped. Chris, who had barely responded, was already deep into the whole game. I could tell. It all became clear as crystal. It was the real reason he couldn't possibly leave hospital – it was so he could maximise the pay-out he would receive. Hecky may well jump all over his dad when he returned home, but there was nothing to stop Chris from hiding out somewhere else. That was where my planned conversation ended. I didn't bother to suggest he bunk down at his parent's house, his sister's, or any friend's house. Chris Balls didn't need to say anything, I'd worked out that he *wanted* to stay in the hospital for as long as they would allow it.

Mr Balls' attitude was a disappointment – compared to how desperate I was to leave. I couldn't understand how to squeeze out a few more hundred, or even a few more thousand pounds, was worth it, when the alternative was to stay miles away from the family in that hospital hellhole.

As I've said before, each to their own.

I returned to bed 4 and felt like my visit, and my thoughtful speech, had been a monumental waste of time and breath. I was all up for people to receive compensation where there had been genuine negligence, but I couldn't support people who took the piss and milked the system on the grounds of utter greed. Maybe I was naïve and needed to latch on to any opportunity – like so many others. It bothered me for a while, as it was better to get upset with that situation than it was to dwell on my own health issues. It dawned on me why Dr Hasim, the burly urologist, had been so passionate in his efforts to evict the guy. He had probably seen plenty of that sort of behaviour over his many years of fisting (I was exaggerating – I mean fingering) patients and he was not going to take any shit from Chris Balls or anyone else. I say anyone else, but he did take some of my shit – not a lot, but just enough for me to notice it on his latex-covered fingers.

Move on Phil, leave that experience behind you.

Fortunately, my mood had been uplifted with the wonderful sound of the lunchtime bell.

After us patients had our lunch, the rebel alliance of Bay 4 had a full get-together. I was proud of my three cell mates. I was proud because they had taken my lead and also refused to wear the standard issue hospital gowns. We had evolved into the Wexham Four, dressed in civilian clothes, ready to take on the establishment and all their bourgeoisie rules and regulations. We held our first meeting by the big window that we had all stared out of since we arrived. Clearly, as the most senior member, I was the self-designated leader of the band of renegades.

Michael and Raj had struck up a conversation before the meeting started, and I joined ranks (because it happened right in front of my bed and because Michael called out to me several times from his chat with Raj). When I got there, we made some brief introductions, and Chris Balls shuffled over in his sliders to complete the foursome and our meeting began. I should add that I was the only member of the Wexham Four that knew we were called the Wexham Four and I was the only member that knew that it was our first official meeting. The other three just thought we were having a casual chat.

There were only two things on the agenda: -

One: How to get out of hospital.

Two: Any Other Business.

Raj told us his story. It gave us all an idea of the type of person that typically infiltrated the inner echelons of the medical world to become one of the Wexham Four.

Young Raj spoke gently and was in a state of confusion because he did not know what was wrong with him, and neither did the doctors, or so it seemed. He was first admitted to the hospital two weeks before with stomach pains that had him doubled over in agony. After ten hours in A&E they kept him in overnight, fed him some painkillers, told him the tests came back fine and sent him home to his mum and dad. After that, his pains settled down over a few days, but whatever it was returned and the same problem flared up again. He went back to A&E, in tears and he told us that he had screamed out in agony. He stayed at the hospital for a further three days, curled up in pain, yet the doctors checked him out and told him that they were not overly concerned and couldn't find anything sinister, so they packed him off, back to mum and dad for a second time.

Raj's plight had not gone away, as the doctors had hoped. I listened to the story and Raj told us that he had returned, once again, to the same hospital for a third time. His guts had been in all sorts of distress and nobody had any idea what the root of the pain and suffering was.

Even though we weren't supposed to start with AOB, the other three members of the Wexham Four did their best to crack the mystery that surrounded Raj's illness. Well, I say the other three, but what I really meant is that Chris showed no interest whatsoever, and Michael was fucking clueless, so it was down to me to offer up at least some theories. Apparently there was no food poisoning, no appendicitis, no diverticulitis, no blockage in his tubes, no strange parasite (he hadn't been to some exotic country), no allergic reaction or an intolerance to wheat, lactose or something innocuous to most of the population, and there was no sign of infection or some bacteria gone rogue, definitely not cancer, but the doctors wouldn't even be bold enough to say it was a virus, which, as everyone knew was a failsafe if there was no other diagnosis.

I, too, was baffled. I was more bewildered by the selective coming and going of Raj's pains. As he stood about with the group, he seemed fine and chatted away, admittedly with a quiet, meek demeanour, but he did not look like he was in any pain or discomfort. I had noticed that when the doctors saw him before lunch, he was in all sorts of distress but, soon after they'd left him, he stopped his wails and his fidgeting ceased. He certainly managed to cope well with the lunch that had been served up. Nothing wrong with the boy's appetite.

It was Raj himself that guided our meeting back to item number one – how to get ourselves back home. Except, Raj had no interest in a return home. He wanted to stay at Wexham until they'd cured him.

He announced to the group that he was scared. 'I know what will happen.' He looked at us one at a time to make sure everyone understood his position. 'They will wait until my pain goes, and then they'll send me home. Then...' Raj's eyes became glassy as a build-up of tears threatened to force their way out, '...the pains will start up again and I'll be back. If not tomorrow, then the day after.'

Michael read the situation well; he parked his grin for a few moments and gave a respectful, slow nod towards the tubby Indian before stating the obvious to the full committee. 'That's not good, mate.'

Meeting number one and The Wexham Four had already become divided. We'd split up before we'd even got going – it was a heartbreak. Raj and Chris Balls, the two members on the far side of Bay 4, well, they both wanted to stay. I thought it was ridiculous. At least Michael was on the same page as me.

'How about you, Michael?' I asked, in an attempt to get some reasonable sanity back into the meeting. 'When are they going to let you go home?'

'Not sure, Philip,' Michael responded after a little think. 'Vey took ahrt one of me drains, so I'm down ta two.' He lifted his Iceland bag to prove his case, not that I had X-ray vision. 'It might be tomorrow.' Michael's face showed signs of longing that I completely empathised with as he said, 'I really 'ope that they say I can go 'ome.'

'Yeah. Me too,' were my supportive words. 'You look well enough.'

'Yeah, right. I feel OK. 'Vey said vey might let me go 'ome if I promise to come back in a few days to get vese removed, coz I can't do it meself.' He raised the bag again.

I wondered if the juices inside were fizzed up, what with all the shakes, swings and lifts. 'That sounds positive. My plan is to leave tomorrow; I can't stand it here anymore.' I meant what I said.

'Yeah!' Michael had made one of his characteristic mood changes. He had shifted from sad and beaten down to upbeat and optimistic. 'Me neiver. And if vey try and stop me...' He elevated the bag to support his words. 'I'll smash 'vis bag in the doctor's face!'

We all laughed. Chris, Raj and I cracked up straight away and once Michael realised he'd scored a winner, he joined in with us. It was a moment of bonding, just when I thought the group had become fractured. The laughs were still in the air when a nurse walked into the bay and called out if anyone needed medication or any painkillers.

Raj's mood changed quicker than Michael's. His laughter stopped immediately and he turned his smile into a grimace just as quickly. He grabbed his tummy with both hands, like an invisible force had just punched him in the guts and, in tandem, he yelped, 'Yes! Yes! I need some painkillers.'

I didn't have X-ray vision and I didn't have the super-power to mind read young people, but the reaction from Raj just seemed so bizarre. One minute he laughed and joked with us, and the moment a nurse turned up, he was crippled in agony.

Raj shuffled his way to bed number two and, without official declaration, the meeting was over. Both Chris Balls and Michael requested some drugs from the nurse. Their reasons were probably different, Chris had to develop his compensation case further, and Michael was either in pain (and just refused to show it) or maybe he simply liked the buzz. I declined, as I felt as right as rain. I felt no pain whatsoever from the abomination that lurked and flourished inside me – no pain as it continued its mission to suffocate my entire digestive system. That hidden monster just kept on with its business. It was stealthy. It was silent. It was relentless.

The beast within me was scary. It was a small mercy that it wasn't fast. The more I thought about it – the more I wanted that fucker cut out of me. I considered whether I should ask the specialists if they wouldn't mind a trip to the theatre – to slice me open – and remove my nemesis there and then.

They could find out what the fuck it was made of after it was out.

I concluded my diagnosis of Raj and wondered if the in-house medical experts would have agreed with me – it was a classic case of hypochondria and if not that, then Munchausen Syndrome. No doubt about it, Raj's problem had been a brain-powered mental one.

Football & Chilli

After the Monday afternoon drugs had been dished out, I was finally taken down for my Monday scans. I had waited all day. I knew they were busy – understaffed and overworked – but I was just so frantic to get out, it had me in a constant state of frustration.

Just do the effing tests and then I'll be out of your hair.

The porter arrived with a wheelchair, looked at his folder, and called out my name as a question.

'Yes, that's me,' I replied, pleased that my next step to freedom was underway.

'I'm here to take you for an X-ray,' the friendly porter announced.

I threw my book on to my tray, leapt out of bed and into the seat.

'Let's roll!' I shouted in excitement. It was something to do, which broke the monotony, but more importantly, it was a step to complete all the tests, the prods, and pokes. I think the porter had a cheeky smile under that facemask, so it must have been a change to cart someone about that was lively and, dare I say, positive.

As I was wheeled out of the lift on the ground floor, I realised that in my excitement, I had forgotten how late it had got in the day. As we trundled along the now familiar route, I was concerned that it was 3:50pm. Ali would call in ten minutes, exactly as we'd planned. I thought the situation through – a missed call would cause some distress for Ali. She would start to worry, no doubt about it. I had it in my mind that she would automatically think the worst if she couldn't contact me. My phone would ring out once, twice, maybe three times. She would text me, she would try to video call and then, if, after ten minutes (possibly giving me the benefit of the doubt with an untimely toilet break) and I was still missing in action, she would switch to worry mode. It had become so important for me to do my utmost to avoid any unnecessary stress for Ali, because the last thing I wanted in the world was for my wife to spend a single second of anxiety. She wouldn't know where I was or why I couldn't take her all-important call.

Maybe, I'd be in and out in ten minutes. If so, no problem.

Christ, that place, and the situation, had turned me into a basket-case. In my defence, I didn't have much else to occupy my thoughts, but with everything else wrong with me I also had become irrationally neurotic.

They had told me that it was for another chest X-ray. They wanted to make sure my lungs had behaved themselves. Maybe I should have challenged it because I was sure they already had a whole photo album full of X-rays and scans of my chest and abdomen. No harm to double-check that they'd got their tests bang on. As my dear father-in-law once told me during a DIY lesson, *measure twice – cut once*. Wise words that my medical team had already put into practice.

We parked outside the X-ray room. Damn it.

There was going to be a wait – it could have been five minutes – but more likely, fifty.

As soon as I had arrived, I found someone already in the room, booked in to have their photo shoot – I had no idea how long they'd been in there. On top of that, there was a frail, elderly gent that had been wheeled to the same waiting area before me. I gauged it immediately that I would not only miss Ali's call, but I would miss it by a country mile. I estimated that I'd be off-grid for at least half an hour. It felt a bit silly to ask the porter to wheel me back, just to get my mobile, and risk losing my spot in the queue. It also felt unreasonable to ask him to go and fetch it whilst I waited here. Shit, it was a situation that got under my skin quicker than a nurse could stick in a cannula.

I was embarrassed to confess that the madness affected me, and

I did ask the porter, who waited patiently next to me, if I could use his phone. Bless him, his English wasn't great – a low paid migrant worker, part of the backbone of our NHS. I explained to him that I'd left my phone behind, and my wife had planned to call at any minute, and was it possible if I could send a simple text message to her so she wouldn't worry?

His response was instant, and he handed me his phone and said, 'Yes. Please. Text.'

I was immensely grateful, and I let him know as best as I could. Fortunately for me, the folder with my ever-increasing number of A4 sheets of paper that accompanied me everywhere I went, included a section of my personal details (they didn't have clipboards on the end of hospital beds like they used to). Ali was listed as my next of kin and, should everything go tits-up, the powers that be could check the folder and, at the top of page one, find her phone number – just like I was able to do. Years ago, I would have been able to remember phone numbers for at least ten of my most used numbers, but with the advent of smart phones, I could just about manage to remember my own.

Thanks to the generosity of the porter, I sent my message. I did my best to explain within the text that she should ignore the origin of the random number, I was OK, do not worry, and I would call once my X-ray was done and I was back in my bed.

Panic-bomb diffused.

My neurosis had been quenched and the sheer sense of relief washed through my body and untwisted the knot of my intestines that had resembled a set of tangled Christmas fairy lights. I was able to relax, but I hated myself for allowing something so petty to wind me up so much. What had happened to my state of mind? I needed to calm down. Ali was perfectly fine - *just concentrate and get yourself better, Phil.*

I took the full fifty minutes to get my head back in the game. Once I got into the radiographer's photo studio, I found the X-ray procedure had become routine. Well, to us experts, it was routine. It was the type where I had to stand up, with my shirt off, and then I had to press my bare chest against the screen for some topless shots. The radiographer and I went through the process three times. Each time he ran off to hide in his little anti-radiation booth and got frustrated with all his technology because it didn't seem to do what he wanted it to do. He did say after the third go that he did have everything he needed and I was allowed out. I was certain that they could not possibly X-ray me or scan me anymore. I must be done. Any more radiation and I would have glowed green like The Hulk.

The first round, the brutal round one of my toughest fight, must be nearly over. I could sense the bell to signify the end of round one, would be rung soon. *Nearly home, Phil. Nearly home.*

Rather than a hypothetical bell to signify the end of Round One of my debut bout, I returned to Bay 4 to hear the real clang of the dinner bell. It turned out to be almost as tasty as the own-brand Weetabix they had dished up at breakfast.

That's a bit mean – the hospital chilli con carne did have some flavour to it. Obviously, they did their utmost to make it as un-spicy and as bland as they could, but there was something in there, I'd stake 50p that someone must have waved a teaspoon of chilli powder in the kitchen when the meat had been stirred. The rice was plain, white, tasteless, and felt like a damp paper towel in my mouth, it managed to nullify any heat the chilli attempted to radiate. Like all other meals it was functional. I ate it all, as I craved the nutrients that skulked somewhere on the plate, but the truth was, it wasn't enjoyable. I was left disappointed and unsatisfied.

As I finished, I hoped that there was enough of a catalyst, some magical laxative properties, within the ingredients to stir my bowels into some recognisable peristalsis. *Come on*, I said to my intestines, *let's get a move on.* Then I added a caveat – *but do not, I repeat, DO NOT play any stupid pranks in the middle of the night.* I didn't pray too hard for action because I did not want to shit the bed. I gave my guts two windows of opportunity, anytime over the next four hours or, secondly, they'd have to wait until the morning. Nobody liked to have a poo in any toilet other than their own one at home, but if it was the passport to get home tomorrow, I would put in a written request for an enema.

Rather than ask a nurse for a colonic irrigation form, I made a pact with myself. If the chilli proved to be as ineffective as a laxative, as it was unspectacular as a culinary delight, I would be forced to lie in the doctors' faces and boast that I had, indeed, emptied my bowels. No way was an insipid chilli going to stop my release.

Once all our dinner paraphernalia had been cleared away, I told Michael that I'd had the chilli in the hope that I'd be able to deliver a significant poo before the doctors did their rounds in the morning. Michael seemed to be amused rather than disgusted.

'Did you have a puddin', Philip?' Michael asked from his bed, whilst he grinned his life away.

'Strawberry jelly,' I answered. Like the ones I used to get at school forty years ago.

'D'you want summfink else?' Michael had clearly plotted something. He looked out of the top of his head, with an even broader grin as he asked his cheeky question. He wasn't that great at being devious, as he tried to whisper, but his smoker's voice would not dampen the volume of his words. Anyone could have heard him.

Now, I could have closed it down with a *No thanks*, but once again, Michael showed such roguish charm that I couldn't resist and I acted as his foil, rather than revert to my previous prejudiced, asshole self.

'What have you got?' I responded whilst I kept up the pretence of colluded mischief by taking a shifty glance around to see if anyone was around to rumble us.

Michael rummaged around inside a plastic bag. I hoped to God that he wasn't going to pull out a mixed bag of blood and digestive juices.

'MILKY WAY?' he declared with sheer joy, as if such contraband trumped anything he could have possibly had. He waved it in the air, and pulled back, ready to lob it in my direction.

'Nice one. Yes, please.' I didn't particularly want a Milky Way bar. But, I wanted to crush Michael's enthusiasm even less, which is why I accepted.

''Ere yer go, Philip!' Michael barked as he jettisoned the chocolate bar towards me.

'Cheers, mate.' I caught it. It was a pretty good throw and catch between two hospital patients.

In a sign of true appreciation, I opened it and ate it without delay.

It was as sickly-sweet as I remembered from thirty-five years ago or whenever I last had a Milky Way that kids, apparently, could eat between meals without ruining their appetite. Fortunately, there wasn't much of it, since the confectionery manufacturers liked to make their chocolate bars smaller and smaller every year. It was way too sweet but, because it felt a bit rebellious, I confess that I enjoyed it.

In our many previous chats I'd worked out that Michael wasn't interested in the Euros, he wasn't really into football at all. Football was something that became a massive interest (which meant massive love) to me when I was a child. As soon as I was old enough to stand up, Richard being the bossy big brother he was, stuck me in goal so he could blast penalties at me. He would say things like, 'You're really good in goal.' That was Richard at his artful best as he tried to keep me between the sticks rather than let me have a go at taking a penalty – with him in the firing line. One would think that a ball smashed into my face as a toddler would have put me off, but no, I was naturally competitive and all the kids at school and in the roads back home played football until the daylight failed us, so I simply had to join in, or accept a position of outcast. I was never a great footballer (I didn't stay a goalkeeper for long) but I loved the game – I loved to play and, as a good second option, I was happy to watch – whether that be in a stadium or on the box. As an adult, I had successfully used football as my international language, because most countries around the world shared a love for the beautiful game. If I ever struggled to find common ground in a foreign place, football had nearly always saved the day.

Not a common interest with Michael though.

Quite simply, football was not in his culture or something within his peer group. He didn't even know the festival of football was on. Fair play to him though, he could see that I was *into* it and he did his best not to quash my enthusiasm as we entered a strange, and temporary, role reversal.

'If England are playin' vah Germans, ven I'll definitely watch vat,' Michael confirmed, with a determined look, rather than his usual jovial demeanour.

'Well, they're playing tomorrow,' I said in return. 'So, we both HAVE to get ourselves out of this place. If I can't get home, sat down in my chair, with my boys, my family, watching the match with a beer in my hand – there is going to be some serious shit going down here.'

'Yeah!' Michael blazed. His international language was anarchy.

On my tiny phone screen, I was thoroughly entertained as I watched two memorable matches. Spain defeated Croatia five-three, after extra time, and the very much fancied French lost to the Swiss five-four on penalties after a dramatic three-three draw. All the great players missed penalties and the football world witnessed Kylian Mbappé suffer the disappointment, and sheer embarrassment, as he failed to convert his. Don't worry Kylian, at least you were not in hospital.

In between the matches, I had my obs taken. Everything was fine, except the glucose reading from the drop of blood that the nurse had squeezed out of my right index finger, which was ridiculously high. It should have sat somewhere between 6 and 10 and the nurse was surprised as she turned her hand-held machine to me to show me a reading of 17. I quickly clocked on to what had happened.

'This is all your fault, Michael!' I shouted out, so he could hear me.

'What?' Michael called back.

'You and your Milky Bars. I've blown my sugar levels off the scale. Looks like I'm going to have to stay in here another week!'

'Oh,' Michael responded sheepishly, 'Sorry, Philip.'

I had joked about it, but Michael hadn't quite grasped the sarcasm within my accusation. Obviously, the sugar score wasn't his fault but, just for a moment, I had made him feel as though he done something dangerous or reckless to my health. I felt bad that my joke hadn't landed as intended and I wasn't sure I could salvage the situation without also making him feel stupid for being so gullible.

I tried to nip it in the bud. 'I'm only joking. It's not that bad.' I turned to the nurse. 'It isn't that bad, is it?'

'I only take the readings,' she said, but she also gave a brisk shake of her head, which I assumed meant that I would be alright. 'We will check on you later and maybe you will get a better score.'

'Well, why don't we forget to record this little anomaly, so it doesn't affect my wonderful results? I would hate to blame you if they didn't let me go tomorrow because of you and your faulty glucose-measuring machine.' I was all smiles and charm. I hoped it wasn't perceived as all smarm. The nurse didn't say if she would lose the result or not – I knew that she couldn't ignore it, there was no way I could avoid the blip.

She gave me a polite laugh and said, 'There's nothing wrong with my machine.'

Then she left me and my sweet, sugary blood to reflect on a bad result, and what that might mean to the doctors that made all the big decisions. So much for a perfect, uneventful day.

The last couple of hours of Monday were unremarkable. After I'd watched all the football and once again joined in with some childish WhatsApp banter between friends, it was the familiar walk to the bathroom with my trusty washbag and towel. Previous bathroom disasters, schoolboy errors and all other mistakes as the ward newbie were well and truly behind me. My night-time routine had become incredibly efficient. I had mastered the end-of-the-day piss, wash hands, contact lenses out and then it came down to the last job of brushing my teeth. It was not a worry anymore - I had entered a desensitised state where I no longer cared about brushing legionella into my mouth. Desensitised = I did not give a fuck.

My mindset had become stronger and more positive than ever. If Legionnaires, Covid-19 or MRSA hadn't claimed me already, they never would. All those fuckers had had ample opportunity to take me down. Yet, there I was, alive and breathing.

Ali and I exchanged *I love yous* through the magic of digital signals and before I went to sleep, I declared to my wife that I would be home tomorrow.

No matter what.

Promise.

Pinkie promise.

England v Germany Day

I was on one the instant I woke from my sleep. Within moments I focussed on the mission to get home. It was barely 6am but I had established a fool-proof escape plan. Some of it was in my control, but a lot of it was not.

I was certain they would discharge me. They knew I lived only five minutes away should they need a thousandth test to be done and that old infection from the previous week, well that was ancient history. Why could they possibly need to keep me hostage any longer? All I ever heard was how people had to sleep in corridors and, as my brother said back on Friday, hospital beds were as rare as rocking horse shit. Hecky's dad and Raj did not want to leave, but I sure did.

I had a bit of a wait until the doctors delivered their verdict. Three hours for me to kill until their rounds at 10am. The first part of the morning session was easy and regimented. I gathered up my wash things and a fresh set of clothes and headed for the bathroom, thinking that it could and should be my last shower in that place. On my way there I noticed something familiar and yet something different at the same time. As I crept by Michael's bed, I spied that he was fast asleep, no surprises there. Michael slept a lot and he must have been exhausted as he recovered from surgery. What I was most surprised about, and most pleased about, was a certain weight that I felt low down in my belly through to my back. It had been several days, but I was sure that the chilli from the previous night had stirred something within me. I'd given up on straining on the toilet, but because of the sensation, I had to give it my best shot that morning.

Once behind the locked door, I undressed, took some toilet paper to wipe the seat free of germs and dropped it in the bowl. I did it to *line* the bowl and to act as a basic barrier of defence to prevent any (inevitable) backsplash. As much as a big poo was going to be a relief, any backsplash from that communal ill-person's toilet was going to ruin any positive experience.

I sat up as straight as I could, and enlisted gravity to help. I was so grateful that such a perfectly natural process was over in next to no time. I urinated and my body seemed to know what was on the cards next. I only had to squeeze in my belly a little and, simultaneously, I became fully dilated. If it got too bad, I thought, at least I was near the maternity ward and we could always pull the red help cord and ask a midwife to help me with the delivery. Twins, big ones at that, were the bookies' favourites.

Just the barest of pushes and a week's worth of awful food, illness and built-up anxiety whooshed out and left my body. I had feared I would force out a rock-hard series of missiles that threatened to tear through my arse and leave something that would resemble a smoking gun barrel but no, remarkably, I sensed a smoothness that I hadn't expected.

Physical and emotional relief joined my private party. The epic clear out continued and I became slightly concerned that there might be a u-bend blockage situation that was going to need a Dyno-Rod emergency call out. I had previous history on that, but only with my own toilet, so blocking up someone else's toilet would be the most horrific thing imaginable. I reminded myself of the toilet scene in Dumb and Dumber. The noises that I generated were similarly spectacular. Something like a mixture of the tuba from the Jaws theme in the background coupled with a furious mega-beat of jungle house music that polluted the air.

I made the sensible decision to have a technical flush at the midway point. I was overwhelmed by the stench – it was completely unforgiving. It was incredible that all the stress had affected me so badly to cause a stink like somebody had set up an abattoir inside a massive sewer. I made a choke-cum-cough sound to try and clear my airways. The flush seemed to do the trick and after a wait of 30 seconds for Angel Falls to blast away all the foulness, I shuffled back into position. Maybe it was because of the break in action, but I noted that the second half didn't produce quite as many goals as the first. The paperwork required to clean up the messy episode would have been ridiculous; however, I chose to wipe away the worst of it without the need to rub my poor arsehole raw, because there was the shower area right next to me. There was no need to clog up the drains with two and half toilet rolls, when soap and water would get my arse back to an acceptable standard.

James Bond had never had a technical mid-point flush, and certainly wouldn't even bother to check the pan after a similar, noteworthy clear out. If Ian Fleming had ever written about the spy's toilet habits, it would have made sense that Bond would just shit and go. I guess I was a tad more conscientious than James Bond when it came to toilet business.

The second flush was powerful, yet I still felt obliged to take some extra toilet paper to clear the bowl of the hard evidence that remained. It was a careful operation that resulted in more smears than anything else. I tried to clean the last, low-down skid marks without touching the cold-water that lurked in the bowl. My work wasn't perfect, but it was good enough.

Everything else to do with my bathroom visit was a massive success. I managed to get the shower to a perfect temperature and had plenty of shower gel to thoroughly clean my backside, avoiding any future clinker situations. I stayed under the shower for longer than normal, and in a therapeutic sense I let the water wash away my worries. It worked, and I felt pretty good, considering there was every chance I was going to die in a few months.

My routine was now fully mastered so I exited the bathroom fully refreshed and raring to go. A new man, about a stone and a half lighter, ready to take on the world.

I continued to defy my role as a patient and had boycotted my bed. I wouldn't even sit up on it. Instead, I chose my armchair and read my book during that hour-long wait until breakfast was due. I was lucky, the story of some old codgers playing detectives did grab my attention and it took me away from where I sat and into an imaginary world. I wanted to thank the author, Richard Osman, for his talent and humour – I felt like the mental break from all the shit around me helped to keep me sane. As expected, despite the welcome distraction of a good book, the hour did drag somewhat. The patients stirred and one by one got up for the day. I sensed more staff members come and go – the day had started up to join me.

When the breakfast trolley arrived, my expectations were in check, and I was experienced enough to know exactly what to order.

Two biscuits (or whatever the official SI unit was called) of Weetabix (or whatever the equivalent brand was) and full fat milk, toast with Country Life butter and marmalade and a cup of tea. I had now become so institutionalised that it was almost (*almost*, I must emphasise) enjoyable. I took my time and it would have been a lie if I'd said I savoured every mouthful, but with all things considered, it was alright. I had a challenge ahead and it was to keep my spirits up in the mid-morning hours between the breakfast paraphernalia being cleared away and when the doctors came by on their rounds – when I would expect them to deliver my fate.

Michael managed to get himself conscious in time for breakfast. Now that he was down to two drain bags, he seemed positive that they would release him soon.

'Today's the day,' I called out to my favourite gypsy friend.

'Yeah!' Michael growled back as enthusiastic as ever.

'I'm either going to leave nice and peacefully, or everyone will fall out with each other. If they don't discharge me properly, there could be a scene and security will be chucking me out!'

'Ha-ha,' Michael said, and laughed. 'Yeah! We'll do a runnah, Philip! Ha-ha!'

I wondered how I would behave if the team did say that I had to stay in hospital or, even worse, be moved to Hammersmith for *further tests*. I knew I had plenty of rounds to go in my bout, but I had to get home today, it was the only thing that kept me going. I needed the break, to get to my corner, catch my breath, watch the England-Germany match and then I'd be all set and recharged for round 2.

I stood at the side of Michael's bed whilst we conspired our day's activities and I hadn't noticed a male nurse had crept up behind me. He firmly called out my name and startled me.

'Philip Honey!' It was a statement, not a question.

'Yes?' I replied, as a question, not a statement. At the same time, I turned around to find who had called out my name. A nice-looking male nurse, mid-twenties, 5'10", clad in PPE stood firm to face me, square on.

He timed his next move to perfection. As I completed my 180, I looked at the nurse with his right hand holding his left in the air to the side of his face. His eyebrows raised and at the same time he loudly snapped his latex glove on his left hand. It was a fantastic impression of a crazed customs officer getting ready to plunge deeply into a Colombian mule to hunt out packets of Class A drugs. He cocked his head at the same time as if to say, *Oh yeah, buddy! You're mine now.*

That act might not have appealed to all his patients, but I revelled in it. For a moment I was scared that I might have to endure a second prostate examination, but that inkling passed because I 'd been warned that I was due to have (yet another) blood test.

We stared each other down.

Smiles from us both broke the stand-off and he confirmed his intensions.

'Blood Test,' he said whilst raising his eyebrows again.

'Oh, right,' I said, with a smile. 'Come on then, let's get this over and done with.' I moved towards my chair and warned him, 'You'd better get this right. If you discover any unusual results, you need to accidentally lose them because I am going home today no matter what you pull out of me now.'

'Yes, of course,' he said and he also gave me a funny, over-dramatic bow which, I guessed, was to reassure me that he was on my side.

I never found out the expert's name, but it was the most professional, painless, entertaining blood test I have ever had in my life. I had no idea what his trick was, but I honestly did not feel a thing. He took three vials of claret away with him. Whilst I thought, *Give the guy a medal,* I also considered that maybe it was me, that maybe I had reached the point where I had become completely desensitised to needles. Just like all my favourite characters in Trainspotting.

Doctor's Rounds, Again

They were probably called Doctor's Rounds for the obvious reason, but to me they were named so because they resembled 3 minutes of punishment in the boxing ring. It was 9:38am (not that I was obsessed with the time or anything) and, praise the Lord, they came to see me (KO me?) first.

More than ready, my holdall was sat on the end of my bed, fully packed and zipped up. I hoped my presumptuous, determined actions would be viewed as positive rather than an annoyance. Dr Nikolaidis, two junior doctors and the head nurse (matron?) stood there, and the main man did not hang about.

'Good morning, Philip,' the senior doctor said.

I gave them all a similar greeting and awaited my fate.

'We are pleased enough with your blood tests to say that we can discharge you today.'

Fuuuuuuuucking yessssssssssssssss!

Hallelujah!

That was all I wanted to hear. I'd made it through. I had taken a lot of shit. A hell of a lot of shit, and finally there was a bold light that shone from the end of that torturous tunnel.

The good doctor talked some more but I was multi-tasking – I half-listened to his words and at the same time I imagined the message I would immediately send to Ali to let her know the fantastic news I'd craved for days.

'Because you live locally, we can let you go home but if you begin to feel ill again you must call the number here,' he said and pointed at a phone number on the front of my A4 folder – the folder that seemed to get fatter each day with more pages of results and other information. 'And come straight back in.'

Of course, I would come back – but I would have to be very ill...

I let Dr Nikolaidis continue.

'There will be an MDT meeting to discuss your case tomorrow and that means that the very best people at Hammersmith will decide what treatment is going to work best for you.'

I could tell that the MDT meeting sounded important, probably by the way the doctor had emphasised his words. The fact that they had planned to squeeze lil' ol' me into their important schedule did flash up as something I should probably be scared to death over – but I was also extremely relieved and excited. It was a strange concoction of emotions.

I was going home!

Treatment? I figured that it meant they planned to zap me within a millimetre of my life with chemo. Whatever, I had already pushed that frightening thought to just outside the gates of hell.

At the very least I'd be alive for the rest of the Euros – and have a fucking decent cup of tea, hold my children, and tell them and Ali that I loved them – all from the comfort of my own house, my own home... they were just some of the dozens of thoughts that raced through me.

'The team will contact you to arrange some other tests with you. I'm sure they will invite you in for a colonoscopy and ultimately a biopsy to find out exactly what we are dealing with.'

Invite me? His attempt to make a session of having a camera shoved up my bum sound like a party failed, miserably.

'For now, we need our in-house pharmacy to give you some medication to take home because we need you to finish the course of antibiotics over the next three days. Other than that, we will sort out your discharge paperwork and then you can get yourself home.'

The doctor had a happy tone, I was sure he had a smile under that facemask.

Bollocks to the cliché, Dr Nikolaidis's words were music to my ears. That doctors' visit couldn't have gone any sweeter. The brutality of round one was nearly at an end. Rocky Balboa (me) could sense the official with the bell – I could picture him reach up to hold the clanger ready to signify the end with a loud DING DING.

'Thank you, Doctor,' I replied, although it was a fast jumble of words as I exhaled in joyous relief. I hadn't noticed that I had held my breath in anticipation as he'd begun his speech. Then I couldn't help myself, and I blurted out my plea. 'I know you are all very, very busy, but is there any chance you could arrange the paperwork this morning? Only, there's an important football match on this evening and I am desperate to get home.'

I'd learnt enough through previous experiences of hospitals to know that the process of being discharged was not the five minute thing that it should be.

The process should mean someone jumps on a computer to fill in the patients details (scan the barcode on their wristband?), print off what would have been a standard form, get the main guy to sign it at the bottom, then hand it to the patient and finally, send them packing as soon as possible because some poor bugger was lying on a gurney in the corridor, with several others, desperate for a bed.

Fair enough, there was probably a bit more to it, but that was essentially it. What really happened was that there tended to be hours and hours (a whole working day) in between them saying, 'You're going home', and it actually materialising. I've always found it to be a painful and long wait, and I knew I would be bored out of my skull, so I was determined to do my utmost to speed everything (everyone) up as best as I could.

My charm had worked on him, and his (hidden) smile continued – Dr Nikolaidis understood what was important to me.

He turned to young Jane, the junior doctor that hastily wrote all of that down on her clipboard. 'Jane, can you see if you can complete Mr Honey's discharge papers straight after rounds?' Dr Nikolaidis then turned back to me, 'We can't have you missing the England game, can we?'

Perfect.

Despite the underlying gravity of my situation, I jumped all over the small mercy that the day had brought me. I was going home. I couldn't wait to share the news with Ali.

Before they all left me to arrange for my return home, I proudly announced my morning's work to the crowd.

'Oh, in case you need it for your notes, I had a big poo this morning as well.'

A silence descended within the group, maybe they waited for me to provide further details (like names and weights). I looked from Dr Nikolaidis and then to Jane. It was Jane that broke our eye contact – she looked down and wrote some more notes. I was sure she had noted down the words 'Big Poo' to confirm to anyone that read my case notes that my body had become, like the Death Star, fully operational.

Dr Nikolaidis cracked first. 'That is good to hear.' There were smiles all around at the joyous occasion. 'It sounds like you are keeping to your side of the bargain. Just keep getting better and we will be back later to let you know what the next steps will be.'

I gave some sincere thanks to Dr Nikolaidis and his team and they left me with a flurry of happy goodbyes.

As soon as they were gone, I grabbed my phone. Ali received a message from me; I was so excited and elated that I was able to send such an uplifting text:

> Green Light. Just sorting times out
> I
> Am
> Home
> With you in my arms
> Very
> Soon x

Ali responded instantly, to check it was for real and I felt on a massive high to say that it was all true and that my bags were packed anyway, so their decision would have been irrelevant. I told her to be on standby, with an appreciation that it was only 10am and I might not physically leave for a few hours. I could tell that Ali was as relived and joyous as I was.

The race to leave – Operation Escape – was on.

I needed some inside help to make sure my discharge was hurried along at every step. There was a lady at reception that gave me the impression that she was in charge of anything to do with level 2. Whether she had any authority or not, did not matter to me. She wasn't friendly, she was deadly serious. Her air of self-importance was laced with *I do not take any crap from anyone*. I figured she was admin and might not have any medical qualifications, which was OK with me. I just needed efficiency and she reeked of it. On previous walks to the lift, I'd made the effort of being friendly, so I had made some small talk, and I also noticed her name tag said Mrs Z Khan. If my release seemed to be on the slow side, Mrs Khan would be the ideal person to inject some much needed urgency. She was the sort of person that didn't go to work to make friends, but instead, she went to work to get results. She probably pissed off all her colleagues, and yet she would be my go-to person that day.

The England match wasn't scheduled to kick off at a reasonable 7:30pm, but instead it was set a touch too early at 5pm, and whilst six hours seemed more than do-able, I did not want to let my situation drift away into the afternoon. I decided to wait until lunch time – the doctors' rounds would have been completed by then, and I could then chase up the paperwork. I would be nice about it, friendly, jokey, but if I had to turn nasty, I would.

I had evolved into the World's Nosiest Eavesdropper. I never realised how much I would enjoy my new favourite hobby. Michael's team of doctors dished out a similar verdict to what my specialist team had given me. They had turned him on his side and dragged out the penultimate drain from him. It was a procedure I had to imagine as the privacy curtain was always in place when the doctors were in town. Those flimsy curtains didn't have the best acoustic properties so where my eyes had no information to gather for me, my ears picked up the slack and I could truly picture the whole scene. The conversation between them ceased and the junior doctor had been given instruction of what to do, so they all (Michael included) concentrated and watched intently.

Somehow, I heard the rubbery squeak of the incredibly long tube as the junior pulled it from deep within the traveller's body. It was punctuated with an unpleasant wet, click-come-pop as the team pulled the tube clear. I imagined a finger-sized bullet hole was left behind as evidence. They might as well have pulled out a chubby, 6-foot-long tapeworm from him. Michael never spoke or even murmured, he just let them get on with the job in hand. I heard them start up their chat again, soon after the drain was out, and they seemed very pleased with themselves. Whilst they congratulated each other, one of them, I assumed the junior again, cleaned the wound and put a fresh dressing in place. I noted there was no need for stitches. The main doctor told Michael that, although they were happy to discharge him, he would have to go back into hospital the following week so they could remove the final drain. All with the assumption that his recovery and progress had moved in the right direction.

As they wrapped things up, I heard Michael mumble out a gruff, 'Fanks.'

They all left him and, just like me, he had become beholden to whenever the discharge papers were officially complete.

Just when everything was on schedule, I had a situation. In my little world, it became the only thing to worry about.

My bookmark was nowhere to be seen.

The little wooden, American footballer bookmark that Lydia had made at school. It held no monetary value whatsoever, but because of the sentiment, it was precious to me. Priceless in the truest sense, and I couldn't find it anywhere. I had pretty much packed everything. My bedside unit was empty. My tray had always been a bit messy since I'd checked in, but it wasn't there, hidden in, or, on my bed, and it wasn't on the armchair. I even looked *under* the bed. It was nowhere to be found. What I did find, was that I entered an obsessive panic.

I had to find my bookmark.

After the previous incorrect accusation, I did not jump to the unfair assumption that Michael had become all light-fingered, again. However, in my mission to track down my property, I probably needed to ask Michael if he'd seen it, without it looking like I didn't trust him. I mean drugs might be one thing, but the poor illiterate bastard certainly had no use for a bookmark.

Katie, the new Bay 4 nurse that had started to look after us since Monday, was lovely. She was definitely someone that would go over and above the call of duty and would, at least, try and help me retrieve my belongings. My timing was as good as perfect. When Katie was near (whilst she checked Michael's obs) and appeared to be at the end of her regular tests, but before she went off to do some life-saving work, I jumped in with my question – one that was also in range of Michael's ears.

'Erm, Katie? Sorry about this. I know you've got loads to do but I've lost my bookmark. It might not sound like a big deal, but my daughter made it for me, and I'd really like to find it before I leave. You haven't seen it have you?'

'Oh, that's a shame. I'm sure it will pop up somewhere. What did it look like?' Katie gave me the response I truly needed.

Michael heard our conversation and I could see him hunt around his stuff to check if there was something in there that he didn't recognise. He drew a blank, like I knew he would.

I described the bookmark to Katie and off she went. I imagined a big pile of lost property stacked high of all sorts of weird and wonderful things left behind by careless patients like me. Most of it would be unwanted junk but maybe, every now and then, something valuable would show up. Despite Katie's upbeat enthusiasm to help, I didn't hold up much hope. My gut feeling was that someone had cleared away all the crap from my tray and my bookmark had got caught up with all the rubbish and it had ended up in a bin, to be lined up for incineration.

What a shame.

Lunch came in the form of cottage pie. It was comically sloppy but did have a trace of heat and a hint of what it should have tasted like, so I managed to scoff down most of it. Dessert was a nice nostalgic blast from the past – I didn't realise they still made Ski yoghurt. I did pause to hope that they hadn't stopped the production of them back in the 1980s. Regardless of the expiry date, the strawberry yoghurt was a pleasant enough way to end what I prayed was going to be my equivalent of the Last Supper. So that I did not jinx my imminent departure, when I was asked, I ordered a chicken curry for dinner. No harm in having an insurance plan when it came to food, right? I had no intention to hang around to see if that curry would ever turn up.

Time dragged its heels, which although boring for me, it gave the professionals enough opportunity to complete all my paperwork. I vowed that I wouldn't make a nuisance of myself until after lunch. Well, lunch was done, so there was no reason not to become a complete and utter pest. Straight after the lady came by to clear away the scraped-out yoghurt pot and the rest of my lunch things, I sprang out of bed and marched off to see Mrs Khan.

She wasn't particularly pleased to see me. I think it was because my release papers were not ready and therefore rather than an apology and a strategy to manage my expectations, she took a highly defensive stance and somehow made me feel like it was all my fault. She was one of those people that wanted to take all the glory whenever there was a positive result and for anything else, it had fuck all to do with her. The truth was, I already knew they weren't done, I just wanted to make her aware that I was well on the case and eventually, after three or four of these little visits, Mrs Khan would be so fucked off with me, that she would move heaven and earth to get my papers signed sealed and delivered. At that point, extreme guerrilla tactics were not beyond me.

I had invested too much emotion in my escape, and I was officially obsessed with it. I knew I would leave later that day, that was a given, so maybe I should have just been cool about it. Let it happen when it happened. But I had set my heart on a time, a target. I needed to be at home to watch the most important match of the year, with my family. There was no way I could accept the alternative – sat in that shitty armchair, with a barely edible curry to eat.

So, it is fair to say, I didn't take the nurse's bombshell particularly well.

'I'm really sorry,' the senior nurse tried to explain, 'it's just that there are some parts to the medication you need, that are not here in the hospital's pharmacy.'

I was speechless; I felt all my plans had rocketed out of the window. She could tell I wasn't ready to reply so she carried on.

'So, we need to find another pharmacy this afternoon to help us sort out your medication and hopefully you will still be discharged today.'

I let the words hang there between us before I asked some questions I didn't want to ask.

'So, what are the chances that the pharmacy sorts out my medication within the next three hours? What can I do to make sure I'm out of here by four o'clock?' I already knew that hospitals worked at a different pace to Amazon Prime. She didn't need to tell me that my chances were slim to nil.

'Aww. It is still possible. But please don't set your heart on it. Sometimes these things take time,' she said and confirmed my suspicions and my fears. She must have been able to detect my devastation. 'I'll do my best to find out what they can do, and we'll let you know.' And with her message delivered, she left me to stew on it.

I sat in my chair and felt empty. It was as if all the joy in the world (or my world at least) had been exterminated. I needed to get to my corner – I needed a break from the punishment of round one – and I feared I had nothing left in the tank to keep my mental well-being on track. I was scared that another day (one final punch) would break me.

Was the quest to leave efficiently too much to ask for? I'd never felt so deflated in all my life. Despite what the nurse said, I had completely set my heart on it. To get home, in time for the match, was exactly how that whole fucked up death sentence episode was supposed to end.

My newest friends, denial and shock, deserted me when I needed them most and they shuffled aside and made room for despair and disappointment. The emotion overwhelmed me; I thought my experiences had made me stronger and that a few more hours added to my sentence would not affect me quite so powerfully. But it did affect me.

My sense of humour didn't dig me out of the misery either.

I cracked and, alone in my armchair, I sobbed.

My cry was quiet; I didn't want to alert anyone. The dividing curtain was in place, so I did have privacy. I let the emotion manifest itself as tears that pushed out from my eyes. I couldn't remember the last time I'd cried from utter sadness; it had been too many years to count. Fuck! I couldn't hold back how upset I felt. It seemed bizarre that I cried over the 'not going home as planned' situation more than 'you have a tumour on your pancreas' news – but there it was.

Mid-cry, a visitor appeared from behind the curtain.

I looked up to see Chrissy, the Macmillan Nurse. She must have seen an upset patient in front of her a hundred times. Her eyes brimmed with instant sympathy.

I swear her head was slightly tilted.

'Oh. I'm sorry. Are you ok? Did you want some time on your own?'

It was a weird moment for me. It had become so vital for me to be strong and positive, whether it was an illusion or not, I couldn't have anyone (me included) witness a crack in my facade. I thought, oh shit – Chrissy thinks that I've broken down and in pieces over my realisation that my life had all-of-a-sudden come to a dramatic end. Strangely, that wasn't the case. I cried because I was going to miss the England-Germany match, *which was clearly way more important.*

'Oh no! It's alright,' I blubbered in response, 'I'm not crying because of that.' Christ knows why I believed Chrissy had the power to read minds and therefore knew what I meant by 'that'. She looked back at me, no doubt an expert in listening and she waited before she jumped in. I quickly decided that I should clarify why I had cried. Because I now had company, so I regained a bit of composure and a smidgen of dignity.

'It's...um, it's just that I really wanted to be at home, with the family, to watch the football this evening and they have just told me that this isn't going to happen.' I sniffled pathetically.

Chrissy gave me her slow, expert nod and behind her mask I knew there was a warm smile that radiated comfort rather than happiness. I guessed she knew exactly what was going on. She understood exactly why I, a middle-aged man, had become a blubbering mess over something so utterly petty as a football match. I probably wasn't her first customer that used the art of distraction on themselves. I'd chosen to focus on something relatively insignificant whilst the doors of hell had been smashed wide open, waiting for me to accept the unwanted invitation to enter and face whatever music played inside.

'Really?' said Chrissy. 'What have they told you? I'm here because they've said you're leaving today.'

Although nothing had changed, my emotional state had started to calm down and slowly return to normal. I explained the situation that I might still leave that day but, with the medication not being ready in time, I would miss the football. Chrissy couldn't have been more sympathetic. I didn't want to read too much into her actions. It felt a bit like she was going to pull out all the stops to satisfy a dying man's last wish. OK, she didn't drive off to the local Boots and demand they make up some pills for me that instant, but she did convince me that she would speak to her people and that I must not worry, she would get everything sorted – and I'd be out in time for the match.

With a new flicker of hope ignited, I felt happier, and I thanked Chrissy. I didn't tell her, but I couldn't allow myself to believe 100% that it would be sorted. With my damaged expectations lowered; I'd only believe it when it happened.

Before she left to salvage my ruined day, Chrissy informed me about my next steps. She reconfirmed what Dr Nikolaidis had said about the Multi-Disciplinary Team meeting that would happen in a couple of days and once the experts had discussed all my tests, scans, and everything else, they would have an intense brainstorming session, and develop a plan of attack for me. Chrissy said she would attend the meeting and if it wasn't her for some reason, someone else from the Macmillan team would call me straight after as they were now my conduit for all communication. Chrissy once again asked me if I felt alright, which I was, and she reassured me that if I had any concerns, questions, worries or whatever, I should call their number on the business card she had given me on that fateful Saturday.

I felt lighter after my cry. Some say that it was a good thing to let it all out. What it did was give me a metaphorical slap around the face and to put some proper perspective into the whole situation. Although I no longer jumped around like an excited child at Christmas, I hadn't completely given up on my escape plan. Plan B was to remain calm and reasonable, and then push through with my release and get out as soon as the authorities would allow. Que sera, sera.

The ups and downs of that crazy day surprised me again. Five minutes after I had sobbed in despair, I was uplifted with delight. No, they hadn't evicted me with immediate effect, but Katie bounded over and from behind her back, proudly handed me the American footballer bookmark that had mysteriously gone missing. She was so excited, and almost as pleased as I was. Sometimes it was just the smallest things that could mean so much. I felt a bit guilty that she might have spent several precious minutes to hunt down a bloody bookmark, and I hoped that nobody died during her watch (they didn't). I was a bit confused with her story, but essentially someone *had* cleared it away, but it hadn't quite made it into the big bins that all the catering rubbish ended up in. She'd clocked it by pure chance and instantly knew it was what I had described to her that morning. I wasn't one for big shows of excitement, but I did my best to let Katie know how overjoyed I was that it was back with me. Katie understood, and she told me of her son and how silly little things that he made for her, like a picture or a card, which cost nothing except time, love and thoughtfulness meant more to her than anything else in the world. She was not on her own with that one, and I would have thought that all parents of young children would have felt the same. I was delighted that my bookmark was safe with me rather than it being trundled on its way to a landfill site - to the outskirts of Slough.

After I thanked Katie again and again, she stayed for a little while and both Michael and I spoke with her about how incredible we thought the nursing staff, including her, had been. Obviously, all three of us agreed that they should be paid a lot more money for all the crap (quite often literally) they had to put up with and then there was the ridiculous length of the shifts and the sheer responsibility. Before Katie left, she gave us her take on what it was like when the Covid pandemic took its grip within the hospital. Katie hadn't offered it up initially, but we had quizzed her and she let on how frightening it was, and how she and everyone there were immediately overwhelmed with the magnitude of the terror. It seemed every staff member had taken a tour of duty on the special wards, and the amount of relentless death seen by them was beyond comprehension. Michael retold his story of when he escaped the hospital because he was so scared. After I'd heard their horror stories, had I been there, I would have sprinted out of those automatic doors alongside Michael. With IV drips and everything else, being dragged behind me, like cans clanging from the back of a newlyweds' car.

Lots of different people came to see me, and they seemed to come and go continually. They were there to make their final checks on me – was I all ready for take-off? Good, keep on with the checks, the sooner it was all sorted, the better. The junior doctor I'd seen that morning came. She was amused that I had packed up my bags, had my shoes on and had been ready to leave since her team had seen me three hours before.

'I hear you have been a model patient,' she said, her voice cheery.

'I've been on my best behaviour since I got here. I've been a very patient patient,' I joked. 'I hoped that it would help with my early release. But if not, then I am prepared to switch tactics and if that means security wants to jump on me and chuck me out of the building, then I'd be equally happy with that.'

The doctor gave me a polite chuckle and said, 'You won't have to resort to that. I'm here to take a final blood test and also to remove your cannulas if that is alright?'

As much as my million-and-first blood test bored me, I was overjoyed that the two cannulas would, finally, be removed. They had continued to be uncomfortable, and I had been constantly reminded of their presence as I knocked them on something, paranoid that I'd dislodge them. They had become a symbol of illness, of being hospitalised and to have them removed was my equivalent of an electronic tag being taken off my ankle.

'Yes, of course,' I confirmed with my most pleasant tone. 'That all sounds good to me. I have to warn you though.' I don't think she expected a warning, and she looked back at me. 'I had a blood test this morning and it was the best one I've ever had in my life. So, the challenge is on to beat it. Good luck!'

The junior doctor took the bait and geared herself up to give me her best shot. I let her do her thing in silence and looked away as the needle entered my arm. Hopefully, for the final time. I held the cotton wool swab in place once it was all over. I laughed to myself as I thought about the ridiculous amounts of needles and cannulas that had punctured my arms in the last week. The sticky plasters and, unfortunately, the bruises were reminders of the turmoil – displayed within the crooks of both of my elbows.

'How was that?' the doctor asked me, fishing for a five-star TripAdvisor review.

'You know, there is no shame in winning a silver medal,' was my honest appraisal.

'Yeah! I'll take silver!' she joked back to me. Obviously, she was devastated and had to make light of her failure. I let her remove the cannulas and she cleaned me up to that point where I felt like a civilian, a visitor, rather than a resident; one of the many sick patients. I had become normal, ready to be let back into the community.

As she got up to go, I rang out the same warning I'd given anyone that had taken any sample or test data off me. 'If those bloods give us some bad news, can you please let me know first before you tell anyone else? I'll need time to ring the boys up, get 'em to drive over and rescue me.'

'Of course,' was her response. 'I'll let you know straight away!' She left me and my lovely clear arms that sported the look of The Summer of '21 with their purple bruised marble-effect.

31

Coming Out

Wow.

Just when I thought my plans were in tatters, the senior nurse that was present for the rounds earlier that morning, strode over to me. I had figured out a few days before that seniority was directly proportional to the darkness of the blue of their uniforms and this lady was in a navy blue, so I knew she meant business.

'Hello Philip,' she began brightly, 'I have your medication here, so I just need to talk you through it.'

'Really?' I was so surprised that I needed clarification that she had the right person. Normally it was the other way around – I'd been asked to clarify my name every single time there was an injection or a blood test or anything. Not once did they bleep my barcoded bracelet.

She was quite direct with me. 'Yes, really.' She asked me to declare my date of birth and my address which I gladly gave her. I could hardly believe it had happened. I had my medication in my hands. Had the stars in the universe finally lined up for me?

My mouth was agog, as she talked me through one set of pills called Omeprazole, that I needed once a day, 30 minutes to an hour before I ate in the morning. It was to help with digestion with the assumption that I suffered from indigestion or heartburn – which I didn't. Then the matron made a point that I had to complete the final five days of the antibiotics that had got on top of the mystery infection, and these had to be taken three times a day, evenly spread throughout the day. If anyone had watched me receive the drugs, they would have been excused from thinking I looked like a gormless bastard. It was just that I listened intently (and gratefully), and I really wanted to understand and take on board all of her instructions.

Despite my initial concentration, I multi-tasked and I listened attentively whilst I dared to imagine a walk through the automatic hospital doors. The excitement made it hard to focus on functional stuff.

'They told me that they didn't have this medication here. They said it wouldn't be ready for me today.' I still had to check that the escape plan had all come together.

'Well, *THEY* were wrong.' My hero matron concluded matters. She patted the white paper bag that contained my drugs. 'Now that you have this, we just have to get the discharge signed off and then you can go.'

'Thank you so much, thank you.' I could have grabbed and kissed her. Through her facemask of course, I wasn't that reckless.

I knew it wasn't just her. There must have been a chain of people that had shoved my request (my desperate plea) through the various channels to get to that point. If I had kissed that angel, I would have asked her to pass it on to all her colleagues, especially Chrissy. My tears, and my irrational story must have tugged at her heartstrings. In the back of my mind, I was a little suspicious of why I had been given such preferential treatment – but there was no way I wanted to burst the bubble, so I ignored the niggly doubts and let the matron leave my area. As she left, matron said she would say goodbye before I left for good.

Left for good. That sounded so marvellous.

There must have been some snowball effect. All the processes that usually took ages had accelerated to break-neck speed. For that place anyway. I witnessed my escape plan happen in front of me. I had been through a lot of different feelings that day – I felt emotionally drained. I didn't feel ill though, I knew I would soon be in my corner and could begin to recoup my strength. The light at the end of the tunnel shone much brighter.

Ten minutes after I'd been given my medication, Jane the junior doctor, was back with the navy-ranked matron in tow. It was probably the easiest part of their day, maybe the most pleasant, and they knew that their visit would bring joy to the 50-year-old man in front of them. The junior doctor brandished the discharge papers, and to me, those pages were as priceless as the Magna Carta.

'Hello again!' Dr Jane was all twinkly eyed. I think she might have been more shocked than me at the speed of my exit.

'Hello.' I surprised myself at how cool I acted, because inside I had leaped out of my chair and seized the pair of them, but if anyone had seen my official release, they would have thought that the whole discharge business hadn't bothered me a jot. I had either been exceptionally cool or, possibly, shock and denial were back in town to save me from an over-reaction.

Dr Jane handed over the A4 folder that seemed to have way too much information inside it. My (now favourite) young doctor spoke the words I'd desperately longed for. 'Your paperwork is all signed-up and in here, you've got all your medication, so that means that you are free to go. Do you need us to help arrange transport for you, to get home?'

Free to go. Three little words that meant the world to me.

The process had gone like clockwork, even if there was that *no medication* curveball thrown halfway through the plan. I could go home.

'No, thanks. My wife is only five minutes away and I reckon she's sitting in her car waiting for the call.'

'If you are sure, then we can say goodbye and good luck.' Jane had nailed the caring part required by her profession. Matron echoed the 'Good luck' and all that was left for me to do was to thank them both.

I stood up from the chair that was never going to feel my arse again.

'Thank you so much.' I looked from one to the other to evenly share out my gratitude. 'Can I just say how well everyone has looked after me. You have all been incredible and it's impossible for me to thank you all enough. Please pass on my thanks to all your teams.'

'Of course. You're very welcome,' said Jane, and then the pair of them left me to send my text message to Ali.

I had primed Ali with messages since the cannulas came out and the medication had been delivered, so I sent my final message from Wexham Ward 10, Bay 4, Bed 4:

Come and get me Baby! I'll be outside waiting for you! X

With two minutes to say my farewells, Michael stood in front of me, his trusty Iceland bag by his side, just like it had been all week. It had been a bizarre relationship for us both. Somehow, fate had ensured that our lives had merged and, because of what we endured together, we had become friends.

I held out my hand and found Michael's handshake wasn't as firm as I would have liked but I had certainly experienced worse. I let his hand go and resisted the urge to wipe my palm on the backside of my joggers.

'I can't say it has been fun, but I do have to thank you Michael, for helping me through all of this.'

'Same,' replied Michael, just as gruff and as scruffy as when I first met him. 'Fanks for helpin' me too, Philip.'

'Are you getting out today?' I asked Michael the most important question of the day.

'Yeah. I dunno when though. My missus has gotta get someone to look after the girls an' ven get a taxi. So, I probably won't see the football.' Michael's response was dispassionate rather than cool, and he was just pleased that he would be home at some point. 'I just can't wait to get 'ome.' It was funny that all the Wexham Four Rebels were due to leave that same day, but only half of us were happy about it.

My grin was now dumber than Michael's and we stood there and shared a glorious moment. Our dumbass grins were magnetised together. I knew that he was going to mention my roof and he did not let me down.

'Don't forget to give me a call to fix yer roof, Philip.'

'Yeah, of course. I mean, I'll wait for my mate first, but you still need to give me your number.' I knew the exchange of numbers conversation was bound to come up, so I got in there first with the *'Don't call us, we'll call you'* thing.

'Oh Yeah.' Michael beamed as if I'd just given him the contract to re-roof Wembley. I opened my phone and asked him for his number. That relatively simple operation was made more difficult as Michael wasn't too sure what his number was. After about the fifth attempt, we got there and I said I'd give him a call. That was a blatant lie. My traumatic experience had been like a terrible RTA, and I hoped that once I was safely home, I would forget every single moment.

'Yeah, gimme a call next week,' Michael bounced back. His voice blazed with boyish excitement. 'And...and...I can take you out to the Toby Carvery! My treat! God, I need a carvery, Philip! Bring the whole family! Yeah?'

'That sounds so good. I'll give you a call, but you really don't need to treat us.' I still found it difficult to resist the man's infectious eagerness. The only force greater was going to be the collective astonishment and resistance exhibited by Ali and the rest of the family if I were to tell them that we were to meet up with the local travelling community next weekend for a slap-up dinner.

It was time for me to wrap things up before I caved in and accepted Michael's invitation.

'See ya, Michael, and good luck with the stomach and the drains and everything. Keep off those fags and stay healthy for the family, yeah? And thanks again.' I slung my holdall over my left shoulder and strode out of the bay as a free man. With the discharge papers in my possession, I was no longer a patient.

'Bye, Philip,' Michael growled as I departed. I detected a hint of sadness in his farewell.

'Good luck lads!' I bellowed out with some confidence towards Chris Balls and Raj on the other half of the bay as walked through.

'You too, mate!' I heard Chris call back.

I passed Raj, who was in his usual foetal position.

He looked up with wet eyes and gently said, 'Good luck to you, too.'

Poor Raj was not happy about having to vacate the sanctuary of his hospital bed. I, on the other hand, was ecstatic about leaving mine.

Katie was in the lobby, and I stopped for two minutes to thank her for everything, especially for finding my bookmark and because she had looked after us all so well under such difficult times and to say that, in the best possible way, I hoped that I would NEVER, EVER see her again.

Katie laughed and countered by saying that she hoped for exactly the same thing. 'Thanks for being a good patient. Goodbye and good luck!'

I marched to the lift. Mrs Khan wasn't at her desk. Good, that meant there were no more goodbyes to delay my exit.

I poked the button to call the lift and it was already there, as if it knew that it was needed at that precise time. The doors opened to invite me inside. I pushed the green 'G' button and I heard all the mechanics of the lift fire up and begin to work as intended. The shiny doors calmly closed, and the machinery took the big metal box down, and when it arrived at the ground floor, the doors re-opened to release me back into the wild.

I left the building. I strode out through the automatic entrance doors and the warm June air welcomed me back into the real world. The service road, outside of the building, was absent of any cars and was quiet enough for me to hear the chirp of happy birds. I could have stayed at the entrance, where there was a dedicated drop off area for cars and ambulances, but I needed to get away from the place. I made a slow walk eastwards, towards the road entrance, so that I would be picked up sooner, albeit by about two seconds. Being outside felt incredible, just pure exhilaration.

I felt excitement every time a car came into view but each burst of it subsided quickly as I didn't recognise the familiar blue colour of Ali's car. Several cars came and went over the next few minutes. I wasn't overly bothered though because I knew she would show up any moment, and it gave me time to reflect on what I had been through since Thursday night. My thoughts weren't of the inevitable death sentence. In fact, any of the drivers or passengers that came by might have noticed the random guy stood half-way down the service road with a holdall on his shoulder that looked like a hitchhiker, and they might have noticed as he chuckled to himself and looked more like a psychotic madman.

I stared at nothing whilst I reminisced about all the bizarre, strange, and funny moments. Having that extremely invasive anal examination, when I dangled my gown tie-ups in the toilet bowl, I had puked in that bowl whilst being told a frightening sentence of words I never imagined I'd ever hear, and the many conversations I enjoyed with Michael. I thought back to the senior doctor that examined me at the end of that first Friday. She probably knew about my tumour at that point as it was well after my scan. She had given my organs a good squeeze, and I wondered if she had actually found what she had been looking for.

I looked back at the hospital behind me. The people in there had done an outstanding job to care for me and I thought of the poor soul that was now in my bed and considered how that place was just going to keep doing its thing, in the background, while the rest of the (healthy) world carried on with their rat race, oblivious to what really happened to those in desperate need. I shook my head in disbelief that the toughest period of my life was finally over, and that my right-hand man through it all had been a traveller with the disposition, and mentality, of an 8-year-old thief. What a guy. Michael, and the entire hospital experience, had changed my view on life.

As I daydreamed of the immediate future of a hot shower, a strong cup of tea and the enjoyment of watching England stick it to the Krauts, I saw the blue car I longed for. Woo-hoo! There they were!

I heard the car accelerate towards me and I stood up as straight as I could, just to show them (and myself) exactly how strong, positive, and well I was. As a lame dad joke, I stuck out my thumb to hitch a ride.

Ten seconds later and Ali had pulled up to a stop beside me.

The kids were in the back, the front passenger seat left free for their dad.

I grabbed that handle and yanked open the door.

'Hello, Mr Gorgeous,' Ali said and greeted me with the most beautiful smile.

I jumped in and we held each other for a long time, aware that although the first battle was done, there was one hell of a war still to overcome. It felt like time may have stopped for Ali and I for the duration of that powerful hug, we were together in a way that was beyond physical. I felt so loved, so supported, and I knew that if anyone could get through the war, it would be us.

Ali drove us home.

Epilogue

I returned home, to my corner, with round one over.

Further tests confirmed that a stay at Hammersmith Hospital and major surgery was the best option for me and that is what *Pelé Can Wait – Some More* is all about. So, book your visiting time, put on your PPE, and find out how the operation went. Suffice to say, it was bizarre enough to inspire the telling of the entire experience all the way back to the eating of a kebab.

See you on the other side...

Acknowledgements

It seems strange to stop at this half-way point (yes, there is Some More) and thank everyone for their help, advice, and for putting up with me whilst I dedicated my spare time to writing up my experiences. There is a considerable amount of thanks to go to 'The Man in the Next Bed' that gave me such great material whilst we supported each other in hospital. I'll never know quite how we clicked so well, but my gypsy friend, Michael, gave me such ideal distraction from an otherwise overwhelming, and harrowing event. He might not ever discover the magnitude of my genuine gratitude, unless of course, he has since learned how to read. It was one hell of a quirky and brief encounter, but it was one that simply worked.

I'll memorialise my appreciation for everyone else when book two is done and dusted. There are plenty of them, and it has taken long enough.

They can wait.

About the Author

Pelé Can Wait is PS Honey's debut book, split into two heart-warming, painfully true stories.

Not only has he amassed over thirty years of experience as a quantity surveyor in the construction industry, he is also a commissioned artist, has played poker on the World Poker Tour, and was part of Team England's World Chess League online win in 2022. He has been married to Ali for over 25 years and they live in South Buckinghamshire with their three children.

Printed in Great Britain
by Amazon